In Pioneer Days

Grades 2-4

Written by Ruth Solski
Illustrated by Ric Ward

ISBN 1-55035-040-4
In Pioneer Days, SSF1-06
Copyright 1987 S&S Learning Materials
Revised May 2003
15 Dairy Avenue
Napanee, Ontario
K7R 1M4
All Rights Reserved * Printed in Canada
A Division of the Solski Group

Published in Canada by:
S&S Learning Materials
15 Dairy Avenue
Napanee, Ontario
K7R 1M4
www.sslearning.com

Published in the United States by:
T4T Learning Materials
3909 Witmer Road PMB 175
Niagara Falls, New York
14305
www.t4tlearning.com

Look For Other History Units

Item #F1-01   The Amazing Aztecs .... Gr. 5-6
F1-02   Ancient China 5-8
F1-03   Circus Magic 3-4
F1-04   Canada's Native Peoples 7
F1-05   In Days of Yore 4-6
F1-06   In Pioneer Days 2-4
F1-07   All About Trains 3-4
F1-08   All About Boats 2-3
F1-09   All About Planes 2-4
F1-10   Labour Movement in North America 7-10
F1-11   Women & Children Forced Change 7-10
F1-12   Pirates 5-7
F1-13   The Victorian Era 5-8
F1-14   Our Global Heritage 5-7
F1-15   Explorers & Mapmakers of Canada 6-8
F1-16   Aboriginal Peoples of Canada 7-8
F1-17   The Viking Age 4-6
F1-18   Ancient Egypt 4-6
F1-19   Ancient Rome 4-6
F1-20   Exploration 4-6
F1-21   Ancient Greece 4-6
F1-22   North American Natives 2-4
F1-23   Native Peoples of North America 4-6
F1-24   Prehistoric Times 5-7
F1-25   New France, The Founders 7-8
F1-26   World War II 7-10
F1-27   New France, Part 2 7-8
F1-28   Egyptians Today & Yesterday 2-3
F1-29   Klondike Gold Rush 4-6
F1-30   Life in the Middle Ages 7-9
F1-31   Castles & Kings (for learning strategies) 4-6
F1-32   Titanic: A Factual Account 4-6
F2-01   Le Moyen Âge 4-6
F2-02   La vie des pionniers 2-4
F2-03   Notre Héritage Mondial 5-7
F2-04   Les Autochtones du Canada 7
F2-05   Explorateurs et cartographes du Canada 6-8
F2-06   Les Autochtones de l'Amérique du Nord 4-6

Published by:
S&S Learning Materials
15 Dairy Avenue
Napanee, Ontario
K7R 1M4

Distributed in U.S.A. by:
T4T Learning Materials
3909 Witmer Road PMB 175
Niagara Falls, New York
14385

© S&S Learning Materials

SSF1-06

In Pioneer Days

Table of Contents

Expectations 2

Teacher Input Suggestions 2

List of Vocabulary 6

List of Resources 13

Pioneer Information Cards and Reading Follow-Ups 14

Pioneer Word Study Activites 68

Pioneer Sounds Activities 73

Pioneer Language Activities 78

Pioneer Research Activities 83

Pioneer Creative Writing Activities 87

Answer Key 90

In Pioneer Days

Expectations

The students will:

- develop an appreciation of the past and the resourcefulness of our ancestors.

- examine the basic conditions under which a community starts and grows.

- understand the relationship between the environment and family life by learning about ways pioneers utilized the environment for food, clothing, housing and equipment.

- compare a pioneer community to our modern community by observing and learning about farm buildings, family life, a village, ways of earning a living, communication, transportation, government, recreation.

Teacher Input Suggestions

Preliminary Preparations

Collect the following items and make the following arrangements well in advance of teaching the unit.

- reference books on pioneer times from the school library or your local library
- fiction chapter books that pertain to the lives of early pioneer families. One may be read as a novel study or during independent novel reading time
- films, filmstrips, videos that demonstrate the different aspects of early pioneer life
- artifacts that pertain to the era; label them and display them at a "Look but don't touch display"
- costumes that pertain to pioneer children to place at a role playing center
- pictures of pioneer life that took place in different areas of North America for displays and discussions
- a set of slates, some old readers, horn books, quill pens and ink for a pioneer school day

Guest Speakers:

1. Make arrangements to visit a Pioneer Village Museum with your students. The visit may be used as an introduction or as a conclusion to the unit.

2. Invite a local historian, who has collected information and pictures that pertain to your city, town, village or community's early pioneers, to visit your class to share some interesting facts.

3. Invite the curator of a local museum to bring in pioneer artifacts and demonstrate how they were used. If this is not convenient, then set up a time when the class can visit the museum.

4. Plan a trip to visit a local historical house that takes tours and discusses the rooms in the house.

In Pioneer Days

5. Plan to have a Pioneer Day at school. Send home the information early so parents have the opportunity to collect things for a costume.

6. Invite a well known quilt maker to bring in a quilt to show the students. Have her explain how a quilt is made from beginning to end. Perhaps she could teach the students how to complete a quilt block.

Introduction Ideas:

This unit may be introduced in many ways. Here are a few to get you started.

1. Begin reading a novel pertaining to pioneer life. Continue to read the novel throughout the unit.

2. Read the story entitled "Granny's Story" found in the book *A Pioneer Story* written by Barbara Greenwood. The book is published by Kids Can Press and is an excellent resource for the teacher and students. This book has many interesting stories that could be used as introductions to your lessons.

3. Display books at centers or on shelves for the students to read and look through.

4. Set up an interest center. Place an interesting artifact at it. Have the students guess what it is and how it is used. Change the artifact regularly.

5. Display poems about pioneers on chart paper. Around the poems, display pictures of pioneer days. Use the poems for reading activities, choral speaking and memorization.

Vocabulary Charts:

Vocabulary charts should be made for the following topics. On each chart is listed the vocabulary that pertains to it. The vocabulary may be listed by the teacher and then discussed, or the students may brainstorm the words after there has been a discussion of the topic.

The vocabulary should be used to reinforce many phonetic and language skills. Students will use the vocabulary for their stories, journal writing and seatwork.

The vocabulary may be listed under the following headings:

- Early Pioneers
- Clearing the Land
- Early Pioneer Homes
- Pioneer Cooking
- Cooking Equipment
- Pioneer Herbs and Spices
- Pioneer Foods
- Pioneer Farming
- Pioneer Farm Buildings
- Pioneer Transportation

- Pioneer Farm Animals
- Pioneer Lighting
- Pioneer Cleanliness
- Pioneer Hunting, Fishing and Trapping
- Pioneer Clothing
- Pioneer Transportation
- Pioneer Schools
- Pioneer Villages
- Pioneer Health and Medicine

In Pioneer Days

List of Vocabulary

Early Pioneers

immigrants, Europe, British Isles, Germany, France, England, Scotland, Ireland, North America, Canada, The United States, peasants, poor people, persecuted for religious beliefs, sailing ships, Atlantic Ocean, seasick, scurvy, cholera, died, buried at sea, hardships, difficult voyage, explorers, steerage, destination, passengers

Clearing the Land

land grant, clear, shelter, tent, lean-to, logging bee, axes, oxen, cut down, chop, haul, burn, underbrush, choppers, drag stumps, backwoods, bush, wilderness

Early Pioneer Homes

log cabin, one room, loghouse, loggers, lumbermen, build, logs, notched, mud, clay, sand, cracks, roof, trees, saplings, bark, door, window, fireplace, furniture, dirt floor, plank house, frame, wooden floors, many rooms, stones, masons, carpenters, mortar, wooden shingles, shutters, sod house, prairie pioneer, leaked

Inside the Early Pioneer Home

small, one or two rooms, fireplace, heat, light, bake oven, embers, furniture, simple, table, chairs, benches, stools, mud floor, cupboards, jack beds, cushions, braided rugs, loft, trundle bed, trenchers, barrels, ladle, churn, cradle, broom, candles

Pioneer Cooking

sift, heat, brown, simmer, cut, scald, melt, wash, grease, ladle, grate, boil, pare, ferment, strain, stuff, beat, season, slice, thicken, blend, bake, pour, beat, fold, fry, cook, preserve, shake, sprinkle, mix, baste, stir, coat, slit, press, smoke, roll, knead, pickle, pound, grind, salt, churn

Pioneer Cooking Equipment

colander, churn, griddle, bake oven, grill iron, mould, crocks, cleaver, fireplace, box stove, hooks, trammel, trivet, skimmer, wooden bowls, firkin, ladle, crane, andirons, skillet, print, paddle, mincer, apple peeler, coffee mill, mortar, pestle, pots, cauldrons, kettle

Pioneer Spices and Herbs

chives, savory, basil, marjoram, rosemary, rue, ginger, yeast, mint, sage, peppermint, thyme, mace, cinnamon, dill, horseradish, tarragon, nutmeg, allspice, leek, parsley, chervil, borage

Pioneer Foods

soup, stew, cheese, baked beans, croquettes, pemmican, berries, fish, duck, quail, wild turkey, gooseberries, huckleberries, blueberries, strawberries, raspberries, cranberries, chokecherries, plums, maple taffy, mincemeat, mutton, lamb, venison, apple butter, butter, flapjacks, maple sugar, maple syrup, molasses, Johnny cake, corn bread, white bread, gruel, porridge, salt pork, beef, bear, potatoes, corn, pumpkins, squash, carrots, cabbage, wild rice, chicken, goose, eggs,

bread pudding, applesauce, apple cider, buttermilk, moose, partridge, vegetables, hunted, fished, trapped, planted, gathered, bannock, fiddleheads, dandelion greens, turnips, onions, beans, peas, honey

Pioneer Farming

hoe, mattock, plough, harrow, sharp blade, sowing, seed, field, wheat, oats, barley, rye, scattered, broadcasting, droughts, insects, frosts, floods, diseases, hills, fertilizer, fish, squash, pumpkin, beans, root cellar, harvest, reap, grain, scythe, sickle, cradle, stooks, threshed, flail, flailer, chaff, winnowed, wooden, tray, gristmill, hominy block, pestle, quern, grist, millstones, millpond, miller, waterwheel, yoke, harness, rake, shovel, auger, chisel, handsaw, hammer, planer, axes

Pioneer Farm Buildings

barn, chicken coop, implement shed, log house, plank house, smokehouse, icehouse, springhouse, outhouse, hay loft

Pioneer Farm Animals

cows, horses, oxen, sheep, lambs, pigs, chickens, rooster, ducks, geese, dog, cat

Pioneer Lighting

candles, beeswax, tallow, chandler, tin moulds, animal fat, lard, wick, kerosene lamp, oil lamp, lantern, candle snuffers, candle holders, fireplace

Pioneer Cleanliness

soap, lye, tallow, animal fat, ashes, rainwater, bather, wash, wooden tub, clothes, scrubbed, scrub board, beaten, stick, flat irons

Pioneer Hunting, Fishing and Trapping

snowshoes, canoes, lantern fishing, ice fishing, rifle, shotgun, deer, moose, bear, raccoon, porcupine, caribou, bison, squirrel, quail, grouse, geese, partridge, pigeons, duck, spearing, jack light, snare, deadfall, pit trap, trap-line, trap, beaver, muskrat, fox, mink, marten, furs

Pioneer Clothing

wash, shear, fleece, shears, carding, wooden paddles, carders, wool, sliver, spin, drop spindle, walking wheel, bobbin, treadle, flax, niddy noddy, winder, linen, tow, dye, dyes, mordant, urine, weave, loom, weaver, skeins, knitting, hooking, sewing, simple, plain, spinning wheel, cape, bonnet, cloak, dress, apron, petticoat, boots, lace, trousers, mocassins, shoes, homemade, jacket, mittens, socks, hats, scarves

Pioneer Transportation

sailing ship, foot, covered wagon, Conestoga wagon, Red River cart, wagon, birchbark canoe, dugout, bateau, flatboat, raft, sailboat, horseboat, keelboat, steamboat, paddlewheeler, ferry boat, canals, blazed trails, corduroy roads, plank roads, bridges, carriages, buggies, sleighs, stagecoaches, trains, water, land

In Pioneer Days

Pioneer Villages

general store, community, storekeeper, merchant, tradesmen, craftsmen, gristmill, miller, sawmill, carpenter, cooper, wheelwright, wainwright, blacksmith, farrier, pewterer, silversmith, tinsmith, saddle and harness maker, printer, baker, cobbler, shoemaker, weaver, gunsmith, broom-maker, dressmaker, barber, schoolhouse, church

Pioneer Schools

life skills, schoolhouse, logs, dirt floor, backless benches, narrow tables, fireplace, box stove, teacher, strict, mean, nasty, beat, speller, Bible, reader, alphabet, numbers, sums, quill pen, homemade ink, slate, slate pencil, chalk, memorize, recite, punished, dunce cap, strap

Pioneer Health and Medicine

herbs, remedies, diseases, recipes, germs, nutritious, vitamins, scurvy, scarlet fever, typhoid fever, diptheria, tuberculosis, pasteurizing, bacteria, symptoms, fever, vomiting, headaches, coughing, ague, pneumonia, mumps, measles, chicken pox, whooping cough, polio, vaccination, epidemic, contagious, cholera, quarantined, isolated, consumption, sanatoriums, apprenticeship, house call, apothecary, medicines, horseback, horse and buggy, medical bag

Suggested Topics to be Discussed

The following topics may discussed in any order that you wish. There is a Pioneer Information Card and a Pioneer Reading Follow-up Activity for each topic. The sheets may be reproduced and collated, or the Pioneer Information Cards may be put on overheads so they can be read and discussed with the entire class. The students will then complete the Pioneer Reading Activity Sheet.

The Pioneer Information Cards and the Pioneer Reading Follow-up Activities may be placed at a Pioneer Reading Centre. Mount the Information Cards onto construction paper and laminate them. Use file folders to hold the Pioneer Reading Activity Sheets. Attach a copy of each worksheet to the outside of the file folder so the activity can be readily identified by the students. The student will read the Pioneer Information Card (s) and then complete the Pioneer Reading Activity.

- Who Were the Early Pioneers?
- Clearing the Land
- Early Pioneer Homes
- Inside a Pioneer Home
- Planting the Crops
- Harvesting and Milling the Crops
- Farm Animals
- Early Pioneer Food
- Pioneer Cooking and Preserving
- Pioneer Butter and Cheese
- How the Native People Helped the Early Pioneers

- Pioneer Sugar and Spice
- Pioneer Candles and Soap
- Pioneer Hunting, Fishing and Trapping
- Pioneer Clothing
- Traveling in Pioneer Days
- Early Pioneer Children
- Pioneer Village Life
- Early Pioneer Schools
- Pioneer Health and Medicines

In Pioneer Days

Suggested Chart Work:

Many charts may be brainstormed to reinforce the recall of steps taken in the correct sequence to show how something was built, made or completed. These charts may be done in a large group setting or the class may be divided into groups and each group is given a topic to sequence on chart paper.

1. The Pioneers' Trip to a New Land
2. How the Pioneers Cleared the Land
3. How the Settlers Built their First Homes
4. Planting the Crops in Pioneer Times
5. Making Maple Syrup in Pioneer Days
6. Making Butter the Old Fashioned Way
7. How the Pioneers Made Cheese
8. How Soap Was Made in Pioneer Days
9. How Laundry Was Done in Pioneer Days
10. From Sheep to Loom

Comparison Charts:

Any of the following comparison charts may be used with large or small groups. The charts may be made on the chalkboard or on chart paper. You may even want to make one that can be reproduced for your students to use.

a) Comparing a Pioneer Home to a Modern Home

Compare	Pioneer Home	Modern Home
Number of Rooms		
Size of Rooms		
Walls		
Floors		
Windows		
Doors		
Heating		
Cooking		
Furniture		

IN PIONEER DAYS

b) **Comparing Food Preparation in Pioneer Times to Modern Times**

Food	The Settlers	We...
Butter	churned, pressed it into prints, stored it in crocks	buy it at the store wrapped in paper
Milk	milked cows, stored it in pitchers	buy it in cartons
Bread	made the dough and baked it in the oven	buy it at the store in plastic bags
Eggs	collected them from the barn	buy them at the store in styrofoam containers
Vegetables	grew them in a garden	buy them at a store or market
Meat	hunted and killed, and preserved it	buy it at a store
Fruit	gathered from the forest	buy it at a store

c) **Comparing the seasonal activities of a pioneer farmer**

Spring	Summer	Fall	Winter

In Pioneer Days

d) _**Surveying the class to see which handicrafts are still practiced at home**_

Survey Chart

Craft	Checks	Total
1. knitting		
2. quilting		
3. embroidery		
4. crocheting		
5. tatting		
6. sewing		
7. spinning		
8. weaving		
9. hooking		
10. braiding		

The most popular handicraft is_____.

e) _**Chart the Pioneer Craftsmen and the Pioneer Products Produced**_

Pioneer Occupation	Pioneer Products
blacksmith	tools, cooking utensils, nails
cooper	barrels, tubs, buckets
wheelright	wheels, rims
wainwright	wagons

f) _List the ways the pioneers traveled on Land and Water_

Pioneer Travel

Land	Water

g) _Compare Pioneer Education with Modern Education_

Schools

Long ago they...	Today we...

Other Activities

1. Plan to have a box social at lunch one day. Discuss what a box social is and the types of foods that would be in the lunch.

2. Establish a cooking center. Use parent volunteers to teach the children how to bake bread and make butter, cheese and Johnny cake.

3. Visit an old cemetery. Observe the dates, names and ages on the stones. Discuss any of the following:

   > Are there any famous people in the cemetery?
   > How many are children?
   > How many were babies who died at birth?
   > Compare the ages of the men and women.
   > Compare the gravestones to the newer ones.

4. Establish a crafts center. Use parent volunteers to teach and assist the students in performing any of the following crafts: knitting, crocheting, braiding, corking, making corn husk dolls, making apple head dolls, sewing quilt blocks, weaving, embroidery and hooking.

In Pioneer Days

List of Resources

Non Fiction

Greenwood, Barbara. <u>A Pioneer Story</u>. Kids Can Press Ltd., Toronto, 1994

Greenwood Barbara. <u>Pioneer Crafts</u>. Kids Can Press, Toronto, 1997

Kalman, Bobbie. <u>Early Settler Life Series</u>. Crabtree Publishing Company, 1982

Early Christmas
Early Stores and Markets
Early Loggers and the Sawmill
Food for the Settler
Early Family Home
Early Settler Storybook
Early Pleasures and Pastimes
Early Health and Medicine

Early Travel
Early Village Life
Early Schools
Early Settler Children
Early Farm Life
Early City Life
Early Artisans
Early Settler Activity Guide

Kalman, Bobbie. <u>Historic Communities</u>. Crabtree Publishing Company, 1990

The Gristmill
Home Crafts
The Kitchen
Visiting a Village
Tools and Gadgets
In the Barn
The General Store
Customs and Traditions

Settler Sayings
A One-Room School
Old Time Toys
Games From Long Ago
Children's Clothing of the 1800s
Fort Life
Pioneer Projects
Pioneer Life from A to Z

Neering, Rosemary. <u>Growth of a Nation Series</u>. Fitzhenry and Whiteside Limited, Toronto

In the Pioneer Home
Building a New Life
Life of the Loyalists

Fiction

Smucker, Barbara. <u>Selina and Bear Paw Quilt</u>. Lester Publishing Limited, Toronto, 1995

Johnston, Tony and DePaola, Tommie. <u>The Quilt Story</u>. Putnam and Grosset Group, 1985

Wilder, Laura Ingalls. <u>My Little House Books</u>. Harper Collins Publisher, 1994

Winter Days in the Big Woods
Dance at Grandpa's
Going to Town
My Little House Songbook

Lalonde, Catherine and Burchell, Louise. <u>Eliza's Best Wednesday</u>. Kids Can Press Ltd., Toronto, 1990

Who Were The Early Pioneers?

Many years ago, North America was first visited by explorers from France, England and Spain. They were searching for a better route to the Indies and Asia. They were also seeking gold. The only valuable items found were fur-bearing animals, plenty of fish and very knowledgeable Native People.

Tales of this new, unsettled land soon reached the ears of many people who were longing to have their own home, or their own farm, or their own business. During the 1800s, Europe and the British Isles had become very overcrowded; land for farming was disappearing and jobs were difficult to find.

At the same time, there was a potato famine in Ireland. Many Irish people were starving and became so ill from diseases that they died. Many Irish peasants were being forced from their homes by wealthy landlords. Their homes were completely destroyed leaving the peasants with only their own personal belongings and no where to live.

In England and Germany, groups of people were being persecuted for their religious beliefs and were being driven from their homes. They chose to come to North America where they could practice their beliefs freely.

Sailing ships carried the new pioneers to North America across the cold, stormy Atlantic Ocean. Poor people could only afford steerage accommodation on the ships. They were kept below deck in the hold for the entire trip. In the steerage area, people had to sleep in berths and use their chests and trunks for tables and seats. This area became very dirty and smelly. The people were often bored as they had nothing to do.

A journey to the new land was not always a happy one. The trip may have lasted twenty days or three months depending upon the weather. Many people never reached their destination as they died from diseases such as cholera or scurvy. Scurvy is a disease caused by the lack of fresh fruit and vegetables in one's diet. The rough waters and the rolling motion of the ship often made passengers seasick.

These early pioneers were ready to deal with all the hardships they would experience. They would have to put all their skills and knowledge to good use and in new ways to suit their new country.

Pioneer Reading Activity One

Read the Information Card entitled *"Who Were the Early Pioneers?"*

Locate and **record** the answers to the following questions with good sentence answers.

1. Who were the first visitors to reach the shores of North America?
   _____
   _____

2. Why did these people come to North America?
   _____
   _____

3. Why did other people want to come and settle in North America?
   (Give five good reasons.)
   a) _____
   _____
   b) _____
   _____
   c) _____
   _____
   d) _____
   _____
   e) _____
   _____

4. Why was the trip to North America an unpleasant experience for the new settlers?
   _____
   _____
   _____
   _____

5. What are "scurvy" and "cholera"?
   _____

6. What causes "scurvy"?
   _____
   _____

Clearing the Land

Once the pioneers had arrived at their grants of land, their first task was to clear the land of trees. They also had to built a shelter of some sort for protection. It was usually a *"tent"* or a *"lean-to"* made of branches and skins.

lean-to

Spring was the best time of the year to cut down the trees. The wood was quite dry and the new leaves helped the burning. The pioneers wanted to clear the land as quickly as possible so they could begin planting their crops. There were three main ways the pioneers could clear their land. They could hold a *"logging bee"*. During a *"logging bee"* nearby neighbours brought their axes and oxen. The pioneers cut down the trees and hauled the logs away. In exchange for their hard work, the pioneer provided his neighbours with food and drink and helped them when they needed it.

Another way to clear the land was to chop down the trees oneself and then set fire to the underbrush. Thirdly, if a pioneer was wealthy enough, special men called "choppers" could be hired to clear the land.

First, all the thick brush was cut away between the trees by the settlers. The brush was piled in heaps for burning. The smaller trees were cut down with an axe and placed on the pile of brush. The larger trees were cut down and dragged to a pile by a team of oxen. These logs would be used later to build a log cabin. The large stumps were left in the ground to rot or were burned out.

The sound of axes rang throughout the forest filling the air. Stinging smoke that curled up from the great piles of burning logs and brush hung heavily over the pioneer's land. The pioneer's wife busily prepared the food for the hungry workers.

Pioneer Reading Activity Two

Read the Information Card entitled *"Clearing the Land"*.

Complete the following activities.

Part A:

Locate and **record** the answers to the following questions with complete sentences.

1. What is a "logging bee"?

_____

_____

_____

_____

2. How does the pioneer farmer pay his neighbours for all their work?

_____

_____

3. What are "choppers"?

_____

_____

_____

Part B:

Number in the correct order the following steps taken by the pioneers to clear their land.

_____ Larger trees were cut down and dragged away to a log pile by a team of oxen.

_____ The thick brush was cut away between the trees first.

_____ The large stumps were left to rot or were burned out.

_____ The brush was piled in heaps for burning.

_____ These logs would be used to build the log cabin.

_____ Smaller trees were cut down and placed on the pile of brush.

Early Pioneer Homes

log cabin

The log cabin was often the first permanent shelter built by the pioneers. It was usually built after the land was cleared and the crops were planted.

The early pioneers had to be loggers and lumbermen. Loggers cut down the trees and lumbermen sold the cut trees to someone who needed the wood. The early settlers did both.

A log cabin was usually a square structure measuring six meters (19 feet) long on all sides and three meters (9 feet) high. Logs were placed one on top of the other. The end of each log was notched at the bottom so that it would fit snugly around the top of the log below. The spaces between the logs were filled with a mixture of mud, clay and sand. It became as hard as cement and kept out the rain and the wind.

The roof of the log cabin was made of small trees or saplings. Large pieces of bark were placed on top of the trees. The rain ran off the roof, along the troughs of bark.

A door and a window were cut out by the pioneer with a handsaw. This was a very difficult task. Many log cabins had a door but no windows. Glass was too expensive and difficult to obtain. The windowpane was usually made of paper dipped in oil to allow light in.

The log cabin's floor was often mud, packed down firmly. Sometimes bark was spread on the mud floor to control the dirt. A pile of stones was placed in the middle of the floor. This acted as a fireplace until a proper one could be built. The smoke went out a hole in the roof.

The furniture in a log cabin was simple but useful. The early settler made most of the things he needed such as tables, chairs, stools, and cupboards. The beds were usually attached to the walls of the cabin. Sometimes colorful cushions were used for decoration. Braided rugs made from old rags were often used on the floor. The entire family used the one room for eating and sleeping. The fireplace was the central part of the log cabin.

Early Pioneer Homes

As the community grew and became richer, the pioneers built better quality homes for their families. Usually there was a sawmill in the area that could cut the logs into planks. In order to build a plankhouse, the settler first put up a frame. Planks were then hauled to the frame and nailed to it. The planks fit very tightly which kept out the wind and the rain. The settlers used the planks to make floors, to divide the house into rooms and to add a second storey to the house. The house could have larger windows and more than one door. The planks were also used to build barns, tool sheds, chicken coops and pigpens.

plank house

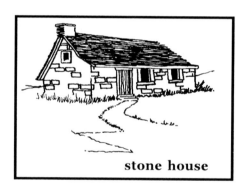
stone house

Not all pioneers built their houses from wood. In some areas they often used stones to build their homes. These people were skilled stone masons and carpenters. They would collect stones from nearby fields and hold them together with mortar. The steep roof was covered with wooden shingles and was curved at the bottom to shed the snow. Shutters were often used on the windows and were closed during storms and to keep the heat in during cold winter nights.

Early pioneers who homesteaded on the prairies built themselves sod houses as lumber and stone was not always available. Sod is the top layer of grass and roots. It was the easiest and cheapest building material that was available to the prairie pioneers. The pioneer first cut strips of sod that was thick and matted. Next he dug a shallow hole for the floor. Along the edges of the hole, strips of sod were piled like bricks, grass side down, to form the walls. Lumber was used to make the door and window frames. A framework of wood was placed across the top of the walls. It too was covered with sod and also hay to make a roof. Sod houses often leaked when it rained.

sod house

Pioneer Reading Activity Three

Read the Information Card entitled *"Early Pioneer Homes"*.

Record the name of the type of pioneer home on the line at the end of the sentence that describes it.

log cabin	plank house	stone house	sod house

1. Sod was the cheapest material used to build this home on the prairie. _____

2. Shutters were often used on windows and were closed during storms and in the winter. _____

3. This house was made of wooden boards cut at a sawmill. _____

4. It was built with logs and had a bark roof and a dirt floor. _____

5. This pioneer house leaked when it rained. _____

6. The pioneers built their first homes after the land was cleared and the crops were planted. _____

7. It was a better home that was divided into rooms with two storeys and wooden floors. _____

8. Strips of grass and roots were cut and piled to build walls. _____

9. In this house, the beds were attached to the walls. _____

10. This house had a steep roof covered with wooden shingles. _____

11. The window in the house was usually made of paper dipped in oil to let light in. _____

12. This house had larger windows and more than one door. _____

Inside a Pioneer Home

The _log cabin_ was small, with only one or two rooms. The largest room was the kitchen which was used for sleeping and working as well as cooking and eating.

The _fireplace_ was the most important feature of the log cabin. It was built of large stones or bricks held together with clay, water and ground limestone on the outside of the cabin. The fireplace was the heart of the pioneer home because it was the stove, the main source of heat and often the main source of light. If the pioneer's wife was fortunate, she would have a special _bake oven_ near the fireplace. It was made of bricks and was heated with embers from the fireplace. The pioneers were careful not to let the fire go out. In those days there were no matches. If the fire did go out the pioneers would borrow burning embers from a neighbour. The embers were carried home in a pot.

The _furniture_ in the early pioneer's log house or cabin was very simple. A short length of a log served as a stool, or a chair. A few planks tied or pegged together made the family table. A rough bench on each side of the table provided a place to sit. The beds were built into the cabin as it was being built. These beds were called _jack beds_ and had no springs or mattresses. The children slept either in a loft above the main room or in a _trundle bed_. A _trundle bed_ was kept under the _jack bed_ during the day and pulled out at night for the children to sleep on.

Jack bed and trundle bed

The early pioneers brought very few things with them and there were no stores nearby in which to buy things, so they made everything they needed by hand. _Plates, spoons, bowls, buckets_ and _brooms_ were made out of wood. Their meals were served on wooden plates called "trenchers" and eaten with spoons. Food was often served from _wooden bowls_ with a hand made _wooden ladle_ or _dipper. Buckets_ for carrying water were made from hollowed out logs. Large logs were used to make _barrels_. Salted meat, fish and flour were stored in the barrels. _Butter churns, moulds_ and _scoops_ were made out of wood as well. A _baby's cradle_ was made from a hollowed out log and planks were used at each end for rockers.

During the winter, while the fields were covered with snow, the pioneer farmer used his free time to make things that were needed for the house and barn. _Brooms_ were made to keep the log house neat and tidy. _Hay forks_ and _shovels_ were carved out of hardwood. The early pioneers also built their own _carts, sleighs_ and _boats_ from wood and leather, as nails were not available.

Trencher and
wooden spoon

Pioneer Reading Activity Four

Burl bowl

Read the Information Card entitled *"Inside a Pioneer Home"*.

Complete each sentence below with words found in the information.

1. The fireplace was the _____ of the pioneer home because it was the _____, and the main source of _____ and _____.

2. The fireplace was _____ of stones or _____ held together with a mixture of _____, _____ and ground _____.

3. The pioneer built _____ into the cabin's _____ called _____ beds.

4. Children slept in a _____ above the main _____ or in a _____ bed.

5. The pioneers made nearly everything they needed by _____ and out of _____.

6. Sometimes the pioneer's wife had a _____ oven made of _____. It was _____ with burning _____ from the fireplace.

7. A log _____ was usually _____ and had _____ or two _____.

8. The pioneers ate their meals from _____ plates called _____ with wooden _____.

9. _____ and _____ were made from _____ out logs.

10. During the _____, the pioneer farmer made things needed for the _____ and _____.

11. The _____ in an early pioneer's home was _____ and _____.

12. Furniture was made out of _____ and parts were _____ and _____ together to make them sturdy.

Pioneer Farming

Planting the Crops

Once the early pioneer had his land cleared of trees, stumps and large boulders, the hard-packed ground had to be prepared for planting. In the early days, the pioneer would break up the land by using a *"hoe"* or a *"mattock"*. He would hack at the hard ground with this tool trying to break up the lumps of earth. If the farmer had *oxen or horses* he could use a *plough* or *harrow* to break up the soil. The plough had a sharp *blade* which cut into the earth and turned it over. It was dragged along the earth by oxen or horses with the farmer walking behind to guide the plough and keep it down in the earth. The *harrow*, a heavy wooden frame with sharp teeth, was drawn across the earth to break up the large clumps of earth. Sometimes the farmer would attach a large *log* behind the oxen. They would pull the log across the field to make it more even.

The next job was *sowing* the seed in the field. Wheat, oats, barley and rye seeds were *scattered* by hand to the right and left as the farmer traveled up and down the field. The seed was usually carried in a bag slung over the farmer's shoulder. This method of planting was called *"broadcasting"* and wasted a great deal of seed but it was the only method pioneer farmers had until seeding machines became available. The pioneer farmer would then attach a large *branch* to the oxen's yoke. The oxen dragged the branch over the sown ground spreading the earth over the seeds. The pioneer farmer waited and hoped for a mixture of rain and sunshine to help his crops grow. Some years, the pioneer farmer lost his crops to drought, insects, frosts, floods and diseases.

The pioneer farmer also planted *corn*. It was planted in *"hills"*. One person hoed up a hill of earth while another person followed along and dropped six seeds into each hill and then covered the seeds with his foot. Sometimes a fish was buried under each hill so the corn would have fertilizer. Later in the season, squash, pumpkin or bean seeds were planted around each corn plant.

Every pioneer farm had a vegetable garden. Turnips, carrots, onions, cabbages, peas and beans were the vegetables that the pioneer grew most often. These vegetables were easy to grow and kept well during the winter. Turnips, carrots and onions were stored in a root cellar. Cabbages were pulled up and left under the snow. Peas and beans were dried and kept all year round.

Pioneer Reading Activity Five

Read the Information Card entitled *"Pioneer Farming - Planting the Crops"*.

Number the sentences in the correct order to tell the steps the pioneer farmer took before he planted his crops

Then **write** the sentences in order to form a paragraph. Remember to indent your paragraph. Copy the sentences neatly and accurately.

_____   Then the oxen pulled a large log across the field to make it level.

_____   The farmer waited and hoped for good weather.

_____   The hard ground was broken up by hand with a hoe, or a plough pulled by oxen was used.

_____   Seed was scattered or "broadcast" by hand to the left and right as the farmer walked up and down the field.

_____   The early pioneer cleared the land of trees, stumps and large rocks.

_____   The oxen dragged a large branch over the sown ground to cover the seed with earth.

_____   A heavy, wooden frame with sharp teeth was drawn across the earth to break up the large clumps of earth.

_____

_____

_____

_____

_____

_____

_____

_____

_____

_____

_____

Pioneer Farming

Harvesting and Milling the Crops

In late August, the wheat would be ripe and ready to harvest. First, the grain had to be cut. It was cut with a *"scythe"* or a *"sickle"*, which were tools with sharp, curved knives. The *"scythe"* was the most useful as it had a longer blade and a longer handle. More grain could be cut with a single stroke. Eventually the *"cradle"* replaced both the *sickle* and the *scythe* as it kept the stalks of grain together in a bundle that could be gathered up easily.

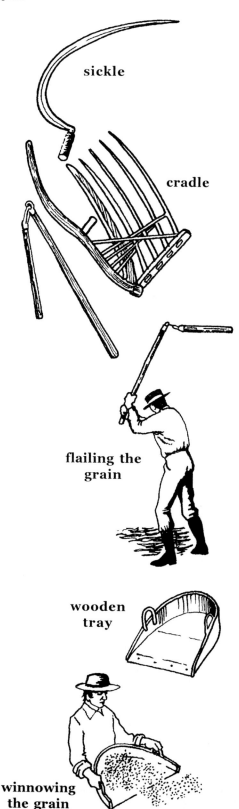

sickle

cradle

flailing the grain

wooden tray

winnowing the grain

One person would cut the grain and one person would follow to gather and bind the grain and leave it standing in *"stooks"*. The stooks were dragged to the barn by oxen before the grain was damaged by rain or frost.

In the barn, the grain had to be *"threshed"*. This meant the small grains had to be shaken out of their hulls and separated from the straw. Early pioneers used a tool called a *"flail"* which was two sticks attached together loosely. One stick was shorter than the other. The grain was spread on the barn floor and then the *"flailer"* (the person using the flail) would hit the grain with his flail and knock the grains loose. Sometimes horses or oxen were used to thresh the grain. They would walk around and around on the grain spread over the barn floor.

After the grain was threshed, the straw was raked away and the grain was then gathered up. Next the grain had to be separated from the *"chaff"*, the little pieces of seed head that were not any good to the farmer. The chaff was removed by a process called *"winnowing"*. The grain and chaff were put into a big wooden tray. The tray was gently shaken in the wind. The heavier grain fell back into the tray while the chaff would be blown away.

Pioneer Farming

Harvesting and Milling the Crop

Not all pioneers lived in an area which had a gristmill nearby. They had to grind their own grains into flour by hand. One method was to use a *"hominy block"* (a hollowed out stump) and a wooden *"pestle"*. The grain was put into the hominy block and the wooden pestle was used to pound the grain. This method worked fairly well with corn or wild rice. Some pioneers used a handmill called a *"quern"*. It was made from two round, flat stones. One person turned the top stone with a wooden handle while a second person poured grain into a central hole. The flour was caught in a basket underneath. These two methods often produced a very coarse flour but often the pioneer had no other choices.

Hominy block and pestle

As settlements gradually grew larger, *"gristmills"* were built. Grain that was good enough to be ground into flour was called *"grist"*. Wheat kernels were extremely hard and required grinding with a great deal of pressure. Gristmills had large, heavy, flat grinding stones. The bigger and heavier the stones, the finer the flour and the greater the quantity that could be processed.

In order to turn these great *"millstones"*, wind power and water power were harnessed. Most North American gristmills were operated by water power. Water was diverted from a river into a *"millpond"* and held there by a dam. When grain was to be ground, the *"miller"* opened the gates in the dam. This allowed water to flow past a *"waterwheel"*, turning it. The wheel turned a shaft that rotated the millstones. While the millstones were turning, the miller poured wheat kernels into a hole in the centre of the stones. The meal that came out of the bottom was sifted to separate the coarse, brown, hard shells of the kernels from the fine, white flour. The coarse, brown particles were called *"shorts"*. Today we call it *"bran"*.

quern

gristmill

The farmer usually paid the miller for his services by giving him ten per cent of his grain. The miller used the flour for his own family needs or sold it for cash in the closest town.

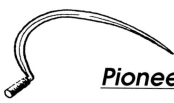

Pioneer Reading Activity Six

Read the Information Cards entitled *"Pioneer Farming - Harvesting and Milling the Crops"*.

Match each word in the box below to its correct meaning. **Record** the word on the line at the end of each one.

stooks	threshing	flail	flailer	scythe
sickle	gristmill	winnowing	hominy block	pestle
millstones	miller	quern	bran	cradle

1. a long, curved knife with a long handle used for cutting grain _____

2. grain that was cut and tied and left standing _____

3. a farm tool made of a long stick and a short stick attached together loosely _____

4. a farm tool, with a long curved blade attached to a short handle, used to cut grain _____

5. the person who hits the wheat with the flail and knocks the grains loose _____

6. a farm tool that could cut grain in large amounts with one stroke _____

7. shaking grains out of their hulls and separating them from the straw _____

8. a place that grinds grain into flour _____

9. a hollowed out stump used to hold grain to be pounded into flour _____

10. separating the grain from the chaff _____

11. a person who operates a gristmill _____

12. coarse, brown particles called "shorts" _____

13. a handmill used by two people to grind grain into flour _____

14. large stones used for grinding grain into flour _____

Pioneer Farming

Farm Animals

Cattle and *sheep* were also brought to North America on the same ships that brought the early pioneers. There were many reasons why animals were important to the pioneers. Animals such as *oxen* and *horses* were used to pull ploughs, sleighs, wagons and carriages. *Dogs* were used to pull small sleds full of wood.

Animals provided food for the pioneers. Every part of a *pig* was turned into something useful. Pigs were very popular. Salt pork was one of the main foods of nearly every settlement and pioneer home. Lard, the soft fat from pigs, was used for candles and soap making. Cattle were kept to supply the pioneer farmer with milk for drinking and to make butter and cheese. Sheep were needed for their meat but more for their wool. It was spun into yarn and then woven to make material for pioneer clothing.

The pioneer farmers also kept *hens, ducks, turkeys* and *geese*. These birds supplied them with eggs and meat. *Geese* were useful barnyard creatures. Their large feather quills were made into pens used as writing tools called quill pens. Goose feathers were used to make pillows and warm mattresses. Many pioneers sold their geese and pigs at the market, but some were also kept for their own food. Eggs were also sold at the general store.

Every farm needed a *watchdog* for protection and to warn of strangers. It was used to chase foxes and other barnyard predators away. Pioneers always wanted a *cat* to catch mice and rats so they wouldn't get into their grain and eat it.

The animals were very useful but they also meant problems. The pioneer had to feed them, especially in the winter when cattle, sheep and horses couldn't graze in the fields. Hay had to be grown, cut and stored in the barns which were often too small. The barns were often too cold and drafty in the winter and many animals would die. The pioneer farmer had to erect fences to keep his animals from wandering off into the woods. Wild animals such as wolves often killed farm animals in the field or if they wandered off into the woods.

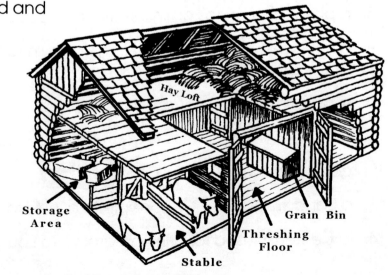

Inside a pioneer barn

Hay Loft

Storage Area

Stable

Threshing Floor

Grain Bin

Pioneer Reading Activity Seven

Read the Information Card entitled *"Pioneer Farming - Farm Animals".*

Farm animals were kept and used in different ways.

On the chart below **list** the ways the animals were useful creatures.

pigs	cattle
_____	_____
_____	_____
_____	_____
_____	_____
_____	_____

hens, ducks, turkeys	geese
_____	_____
_____	_____
_____	_____
_____	_____
_____	_____
_____	_____

horses, oxen	dogs
_____	_____
_____	_____
_____	_____
_____	_____
_____	_____

cat	sheep
_____	_____
_____	_____
_____	_____
_____	_____
_____	_____

Early Pioneer Food

The early pioneers did not bring many supplies with them to their new home. As soon as they reached their section of land they had to search for food. They were very fortunate because the woods and forests were filled with *animals, plants, birds* and *berries*. The lakes, rivers and seas were full of *fish*. The early pioneers hunted, trapped, fished and gathered berries and plants to eat in order to stay alive.

Deer, moose, bear, rabbit, gopher, squirrel and *beaver* were some of the animals that were hunted and trapped for food. *Pheasants, grouse, pigeons, ducks, geese* and *partridges* were added to their meals. *Salmon, trout, herring, bass* and other kinds of fish were caught in the rivers and lakes. All of these animals provided food for the pioneers. Some were not very tasty while others were tough to eat, but all of them could be eaten. The pioneers quickly learned how to cook each type of meat or fish.

The pioneers also kept animals on their farms. The *pork* from pigs was an important meat. Old cows and sheep were sometimes killed but their meat was tough to eat. The easiest way to cook meat was on a spit in front of the fireplace or over a fire. The spit had to be turned regularly so the meat would cook evenly on all sides. Turning the spit was the job a child often had to do. The pioneers also fried and boiled meat or cooked it in stews and pies.

Bread was a very important food for the pioneers. At first they made a type of corn bread from ground cornmeal that they got from the Native People. The Native People taught them how to grow their own corn and pumpkins.

Once the pioneers had harvested their first wheat crops and the grain was ground into flour, they made white bread. Bread was baked in different ways. Fur traders and voyageurs cooked bread in an open pan beside the fire. This type of bread was called *"bannock"*. Pioneers who had their own homes used ovens beside the fireplace in which to bake their bread. Some pioneers used outdoor stone ovens where large loaves of bread could be baked. The pioneers used different types of grains in order to make their bread.

The pioneers found many *fruits* and *vegetables* growing in the wild such as *fiddleheads, wild rice, blackberries, cranberries* and *dandelion greens*. Vegetables such as *cabbage, turnips, carrots, potatoes, onions, beans* and *peas* were popular when the pioneers began planting their own gardens.

The Native People taught the pioneers how to tap sugar maple trees to get *sap*. The sap was boiled down into *syrup* and *sugar*.

SSF1-06

Pioneer Reading Activity Eight

Read the Information Card entitled *"Early Pioneer Food"*.

Record the word *"True"* or *"False"* on the line found after each statement below about pioneer food.

1. The early pioneers found it difficult to find food near their new homes. _____

2. Early pioneer food was often tough and not very tasty. _____

3. The Native People did not like the early pioneers and would not help them out. _____

4. Bread was the most important food in the pioneer diet. _____

5. Bannock is a type of meat that is cooked on a spit over a fire. _____

6. The pioneers had to hunt wild animals and birds for food. _____

7. The pioneers found wild cabbages, turnips and carrots growing in the forests. _____

8. The pioneers used maple syrup and maple sugar to sweeten their foods. _____

9. The easiest way to cook meat was on a spit in front of the fireplace. _____

10. The Native People taught the pioneers how to grow pumpkins and corn. _____

11. The pioneers taught the Native People how to make maple syrup and maple sugar. _____

12. Early pioneers gathered berries and plants, and hunted, trapped and fished in order to stay alive during the early years in North America. _____

Pioneer Cooking and Preserving

The pioneer's wife cooked everything in, on, or near the fireplace at first. Cooking pots and kettles hung from hooks attached to a bar called a *"swing crane"*. The frying pans and cooking utensils all had long handles so hands would not get burned. All the pots and kettles had legs so that they could sit over the fire. *"Trivets"* were three-legged stands on which pans were placed in the fireplace.

Meat was roasted on a spit or hung on a rope near the fire. Stews and soups were cooked in cooking pots and kettles. Bread was baked in a *bake oven* that was built into the side of the fireplace or in a *bake oven* that was built outdoors. Butter was made from fresh milk in a *churn*.

One of the biggest problems the pioneers had was making their food last throughout the year. They *preserved* and *canned* many kinds of food in order to have something to eat during the long, cold winter months. There were several ways to do this. Foods could be *dried*, *salted* or *pickled*, *smoked* or *stored* where the weather would not ruin them such as in an *ice house* or a *root cellar*.

Fish was kept from spoiling by *drying* it in the sun on racks. The pioneers also dried fruits such as apples and peaches. The fruit would be peeled, cored and cut into slices. The slices were then threaded onto strings and the strings were hung out on the outside walls to dry in the sunshine. Boiling water was poured over the slices to soften them so they could be eaten. The liquid was used as a fruit juice for the pioneers to drink.

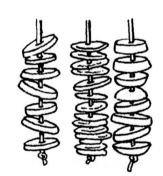

Salting was the most popular method used to keep meat from going bad. The meat was cut into pieces and then put into barrels and covered with a *brine* of salt and water. *Salt pork* was one of the main foods served in pioneer days. A fish such as herring was also salted.

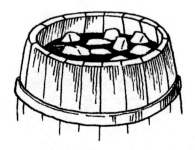

Smoking was another way to prevent food from spoiling. Meat or fish had to be put into a *salted brine* first and then *dried* before it could be smoked. Most pioneer farms had a *smokehouse*. It was a small, log building near the cabin.

Pioneer Cooking and Preserving

A *fire pit* was dug in the floor of the smokehouse and lined with stones or bricks. The meat or fish was suspended by twine or rope from racks attached to the ceiling of the smokehouse. A fire was built in the fire pit. Green wood from oak, alder or hickory trees was used because it burned slowly and gave the best flavour. The fire was kept *smouldering* for up to a week.

Fruits and vegetables such as onions, cucumbers and melons were often *canned* or *preserved* in a brine of water, vinegar, salt and spices. *Vinegar* was made from apples, maple or birch sap or other fruits. Fruits were preserved in jams and jellies. Fruit was cut up and mixed with honey, sugar, cider and cinnamon and stored in covered *crocks*.

Most homes had a *root cellar* in which they stored fruits and vegetables. *Root cellars* were built under the houses or in the sides of hills. A *root cellar* kept the food cool in the summer as well. Cider, pickled meat, pickled vegetables, fruit preserves and eggs were stored in the root cellar. Eggs were coated with *wax* and packed in *ashes, sawdust* or *straw* to keep them fresh.

Food was also stored in *springhouses* and *ice houses*. A *springhouse* was a shed built over a cold, running spring. Butter and cream were stored in crocks and jugs and put into the cold water. Some settlers lowered food in pails into *wells* to keep it cold. *Ice houses* were often built near lakes and rivers. During the winter, ice was cut into blocks and stored in the *ice house*. The *ice house* was used during the summer to store food.

Pioneer Reading Activity Nine

Read the Information Card entitled *"Pioneer Cooking and Preserving"*.

Record the word "**Present**" or the word "**Past**" at the end of each sentence to indicate when the type of cooking took place.

1. The lamb stew was bubbling merrily in the pot hanging on the cooking crane over the hot fire. _____

2. Greg's mother put the roast of beef in the oven of her electric stove to cook for Sunday's dinner. _____

3. Ashley's mother opened a can of tomato soup and heated it in a pot on her gas stove. _____

4. Mary's father cut the pork into pieces and stored them in a brine of salt and water in a wooden barrel. _____

5. The milk was taken from the farm by truck to the dairy to be made into pasteurized milk, butter and cheese. _____

6. Sarah sat on the stool and moved the dasher of the butter churn up and down for thirty minutes. _____

7. Tony's mother unpacked the fruits and vegetables and stored them in the refrigerator to preserve them. _____

8. Willie's father told him to put the crock of butter and the jug of milk in the springhouse to keep it cold. _____

9. Jim and his father cleaned the fish they had caught, wrapped them in tinfoil and stored them in the freezer to eat later. _____

10. In the fall, Mrs. McGregor stored her preserved fruits and vegetables in the root cellar under the log cabin for the winter. _____

11. Lisa's mother's freshly made strawberry jam sat on the kitchen counter in sparkling, glass jars with shiny, gold lids. _____

12. Sarah loved the delicious smell the bread made as it was baking in the bake oven. _____

Pioneer Butter and Cheese

A pioneer family usually kept one or two dairy cows. The cows provided the family with milk to be used to make *butter* and *cheese*. Very little of the *milk* was used for drinking.

Butter is made by mixing and shaking cream. On a pioneer farm this was done in a *"churn"*. Churning causes the *protein coating* wrapped around the *fat globules* to break. The fat globules then stick together making butter.

If butter was running low, the pioneer's wife would leave *fresh milk* out in a shallow pan overnight. During the night the *cream* would rise to the surface, and the next morning skimmed off with a wooden spoon. The cream was left to sit until it was *shiny,* and *slightly sour.* Then it was poured into a churn.

A *churn* looked like a small barrel with a *"dasher"* that was raised or lowered to mix the cream. It would take about thirty minutes to churn the cream into butter. Usually this job was given to a child as young as ten.

When the butter was firm, it was removed from the churn and then washed in cold water. Next it was put into a wooden bowl and squeezed against the sides with a wooden paddle to force out any remaining liquid. Salt could then be added to flavour the butter.

Sometimes the butter was pressed into *butter moulds.* The wooden moulds gave the butter a shape and a fancy design on the top.

Milk was also used to make *cheese.* It was much more difficult to make but lasted longer than butter.

The early settlers made *rennet* by salting and drying the first stomach of a newborn calf or lamb. A piece of rennet was soaked in half a cup of water and then added to the fresh milk. The *rennet* caused the milk to *curdle* and separate into *curds* and *whey.* The *curds* were the solid lumps and the *whey* was the liquid. The curds were separated from the whey and then cut up. Salt could be added.

Cheese press

The curds were then put into a *cheese press* under slight pressure. Over time the pressure was increased until the cheese became a solid block.

Pioneer Reading Activity Ten

Read the Information Card entitled *"Pioneer Butter and Cheese"*.

A) **Number** in the correct order the sentences that tell how to make pioneer butter.

_____ Leave the bowl of cream until it is shiny and slightly sour.

_____ Move the dasher up and down for thirty minutes.

_____ Press the butter into butter moulds.

_____ When the butter is firm, remove it from the churn.

_____ Pour the cream into the butter churn.

_____ Next morning skim off the cream with a wooden spoon into a bowl.

_____ Wash the butter in cold water.

_____ Leave out fresh milk in a shallow pan overnight.

_____ Put the butter into a wooden bowl and squeeze it against the sides with a wooden paddle to force out any liquid.

_____ Add some salt to add flavour.

B) **Number** in the correct order the sentences that tell how to make pioneer cheese.

_____ Put the curds into a cheese press.

_____ Separate the curds (lumps) from the whey (liquid).

_____ Soak a piece of rennet in half a cup of water for a while.

_____ The milk will curdle and separate into curds (lumps) and liquid (whey).

_____ Add some salt for flavour.

_____ Cut up the curds.

_____ Add the water to the fresh milk.

_____ Increase the pressure of the cheese press until the cheese is a solid block.

Pioneer Sugar and Spice

The pioneers lived fairly well with the basic foods that they planted and raised. They had plenty of meat, grains, vegetables and fruits but had very few spices or sugar to improve their taste.

Sage

Some pioneers did bring seeds for *herbs* with them such as horseradish, thyme, marjoram, sage, chives and rosemary. They would plant these herbs in their herb gardens and dry them later to use for flavourings during the winter months. They could not grow such things as pepper, cinnamon, cloves or other spices that grew in hotter climates. These *spices* were brought to places by large ships from far-away countries.

Thyme

The pioneers had no white or brown *sugar* or *molasses* as sugar cane does not grow in North America. They had to buy sugar at a nearby town. *Honey* could also be used to sweeten dishes.

The Native People living in areas where maple trees grew, taught the early pioneers how to make *maple syrup* and *maple sugar*. The *sap* was collected during the middle of the month of March, when the days were mild enough and the nights just frosty enough for the sap to be running in the maple trees.

The pioneer would bore a hole in each maple tree and then hammer in a hollow, wooden, round tube called a *"spile"*. A *wooden bucket* was placed under the spile to catch the sap. Every day the buckets of sap would be emptied into one large barrel and hauled away on a sled to the place in the *sugar bush* where a large fire had been built.

The sap was *poured* into large, black cauldrons or kettles that were hung over the fire. The sap was *boiled* until it became a thin *syrup*. Twigs, bits of bark and other dirt were removed when the thin syrup was poured through a woollen cloth. A piece of pork fat was added later to clean out any other small particles. The fat made scum rise to the top so it could be skimmed off.

Pioneer Sugar and spice

The sap had to be *stirred* constantly so it wouldn't burn. In order to make maple sugar, the sap was boiled over a smaller fire and carefully stirred. The syrup was stored in jugs and maple sugar was packed into wooden boxes or tubs to be used later.

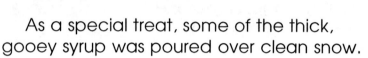

As a special treat, some of the thick, gooey syrup was poured over clean snow. The syrup hardened into *taffy* and the pioneer family had a wonderful treat for all of their hard work.

Since white sugar was expensive to buy and making syrup was hard work, the pioneer was always delighted when a *honey bee tree* was discovered. A honey bee tree could be found by carefully following the path honeybees took in the spring as they traveled back to their nests carrying the nectar taken from flowers. The tree was *marked* and left alone until the bees had filled it with *honey*.

In the autumn, the pioneer family would take crocks, pails, bowls, and wooden tubs on a sled to the honey bee tree. They also took hot coals from the fire in an iron kettle. Wet leaves or cedar boughs were put over the hot coals to make a thick smoke. The *smoke* made the bees sleepy and calm.

The tree was then cut down and everyone worked quickly as they scooped out the *honeycomb* from the tree. Not all of the bees were affected by the smoke so the pioneers still got stung. The sweetness of the *honey* and the *beeswax* that would be used to make candles was worth all the pain caused by the bee stings.

Honey was used as a salve for scrapes and small cuts and as an ingredient in a mixture used to ease a cough and a sore throat.

Pioneer Reading Activity Eleven

Read the Information Cards entitled *"Pioneer Sugar and Spice"*.

Complete each sentence with words from the information.

1. Pioneer food was not very tasty because _____

   _____

2. The pioneers were able to use herbs to flavour their food because

   _____

3. The pioneers did not have white or brown sugar or molasses because

   _____

   _____

4. The pioneers knew how to make maple syrup and maple sugar because

   _____

   _____

5. The best time of the year to collect sap is in March when the days are mild
   and the nights are frosty because _____

   _____

6. The syrup had to be poured through a woollen cloth because _____

   _____

7. The sap had to be stirred constantly because _____

   _____

8. Honey bees were followed by the pioneers because _____

   _____

9. The pioneers made a thick smoke in a pot when they collected the honey
   because _____

   _____

10. The pain from the bee stings was worth it because _____

   _____

   _____

Pioneer Candles and Soap

The evening hours in a pioneer home were lit by the glow of the *fireplace* and the light from *candles*. Most pioneers made their own candles from *"tallow"* (animal fat or lard). The tallow was saved from the animals the pioneers slaughtered to eat. Tallow from cows and sheep was used the most.

Tallow had to be prepared very carefully as candles made from animal fat could go bad after a time. The tallow was boiled in water several times to get rid of the impurities. The fat was then strained to make sure it was as pure as possible. Waxy tallow has a distinct smell so the pioneers added wild ginger, bayberries or fragrant herbs to the hot liquid.

Wicks were tied to a long stick. The *wicks* were dipped into the hot tallow over and over again. Each time the *wicks* were dipped, they were removed and allowed to cool. This process continued until the candles were fat enough. Sometimes the pioneers used *candle moulds* which were faster. The best candles were made from *beeswax* but it was hard to get.

The *"tallow"* that was used to make candles was also used to make soap. *"Lye"* and *"tallow"* were the main ingredients needed to make *soap*. The pioneers had to make the *lye* as well. *Ashes* from the fireplace or stove were saved in a large wooden barrel. The rainwater that was poured over the ashes dissolved them and carried away the lye to a wooden bucket stored under the barrel.

The *lye-water* was emptied into a huge kettle along with the tallow, the fat scraps, drippings and candle ends. The mixture was stirred constantly as it boiled over the fire. Making soap was a very hot task and the fumes from the lye irritated the stirrer's eyes. The liquid thickened and hardened and was cut into blocks to be used for bathing, and for washing dishes and clothes.

Saturday night was *bath time* in a pioneer home. A large wooden tub was filled with hot water that was heated on the fireplace or stove. Chairs were placed around the tub and covered with blankets to provide the bather with privacy and warmth. The bather scrubbed his/her body with a cloth and homemade soap. Every member of the family took turns having a bath in the tub. The pioneers did not bathe as often as we do because they believed it was unhealthy.

Pioneer Reading Activity Twelve

Read the Information Card entitled *"Pioneer Candles and Soap"*.

Each sentence does not have a good beginning. **Locate** the correct beginning for each sentence from the box. **Record** it neatly on the line provided.

1. _____ lit the log cabin at night.

2. _____ to make candles and soap.

3. _____ smell very nice.

4. _____ to a long stick and dipped into the tallow.

5. _____ main ingredients used to make soap.

6. _____ were stored in a large wooden barrel.

7. _____ in the barrel to make lye-water.

8. _____ , drippings and candle ends were boiled in a kettle over the fire.

9. _____ and was cut into blocks.

10. _____ once a week in a big wooden tub in front of the fireplace.

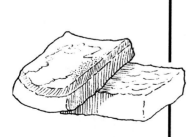

```
• Tallow was used
• Candlewicks were tied
• The rainwater dissolved the ashes
• Candles and the fireplace
• The liquid became thick and hard
• Lye and tallow were the two
• Tallow candles did not
• The ashes from the fireplace
• A pioneer family bathed
• Lye-water, tallow, the fat scraps
```

Pioneer Hunting, Fishing and Trapping

The Native People taught the pioneers many of their hunting, fishing and trapping skills. Hunting and fishing were carried out throughout the year. The Native People taught the pioneers the skill of using canoes in the summer and snowshoes in the winter for hunting. *Lantern fishing* in the summer and *ice-fishing* in the winter were other skills learned from the Native People.

A good shotgun or a good rifle was a valuable pioneer possession. Often this type of hunting weapon was very expensive. Poorer pioneers often had to settle for a gun made by a local gunsmith or blacksmith.

Winter was the best time of the year to hunt. The forests were not as thick and animal tracks could be readily seen in the snow. Deer tracks could be easily found in a forest. The hunter would move very quietly and often hide behind trees. When he was close enough he would raise his rifle carefully and aim at the deer's shoulder as he would only have one shot. If he missed, it would take him so long to reload his rifle that the deer would be gone.

When a pioneer hunter killed an animal, he had to prepare it to bring it back to his family. The animal's head was tied to its feet and a stick of beechwood was put through them. The hunter would then pull the animal across the snow to his home. Sometimes the hunter would have to leave the animal where he had shot it. He would use his hunting knife to remove the deer's head, clean out the animal's inside parts and remove part of its hide. The meat would be wrapped up in the skin and hung from the top of a springy sapling. The meat would hang just out of the reach of wolves and bears. The hunter would return later to retrieve the meat.

The pioneers also hunted smaller animals such as raccoons, porcupines, bears, moose, caribou, bison and squirrels. The early pioneers found squirrels delicious to eat. Birds, such as quail, grouse, geese, partridges, pigeons and ducks, were often hunted and appeared many times on the pioneer dinner table.

The lakes and rivers in North America were filled with a wide variety of fresh water fish. *Spearing fish* was the most common way of catching them. A fisher stood silently near the edge of a river

Pioneer Hunting, Fishing and Trapping

with his spear in hand waiting for a fish to swim by. Swiftly and smoothly the fish would be speared. This method of fishing also took place at night in a boat. Two fishers would go out in a light rowboat. The spearman sat in the bow of the boat with his spear made of white ash. The spear was three metres (ten feet) long and had three sharp prongs at its end.

A stick about a metre and a half long (five feet) was attached to the bow of the boat. A *fire pot*, filled with pitch pine sticks, hung from the end of this pole. A fire was lit in the *fire pot* and the light lit up a large area of the river to a depth of over three metres (ten feet). This fire light was called a *"jack light"*. The fishers would drift slowly downstream. The spearman kept a careful watch for fish. Upon seeing one, he would carefully aim his throw for just behind the head of the fish. During night-fishing, a fisher had to keep his balance. One clumsy move could upset the boat and into the cold water would go the equipment, the fishers and all the fish they had previously caught.

During the winter, fish were caught from a hole in the ice. The fisher would cut a hole in the ice, and sit with a line and a baited hook beside it. The fisher would be wrapped in a blanket or a buffalo robe to keep warm. The most common fish caught using this method was trout.

The Native People taught the early pioneers everything that they knew about trapping animals. They taught them how to make *snares, deadfalls,* and *pit traps.* Animals such as the beaver, muskrat, fox, mink and marten were trapped for their fine coats.

The pioneer trapper had to learn to read animal signs left on the ground or in the snow. He had to know which routes the animals followed regularly. Along these routes, the pioneer trapper laid his traps. This series of traps was called his *"trap-line"*.

Most trapping was done in the winter. A pioneer farmer could work his trap-line in the winter and work on his farm in the summer. The Native People taught the pioneers how to scrape and tan the hides and furs. In the spring the furs were taken to a trading post or nearby town to be traded for goods that were needed by the pioneer or sold for money.

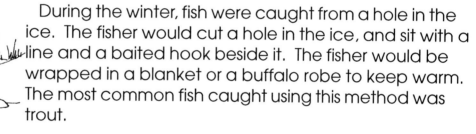

Pioneer Reading Activity Thirteen

Read the Information Cards entitled *"Pioneer Hunting, Fishing and Trapping"*.

The Native People taught the pioneers many skills to help them hunt, fish and trap in order to survive.

Classify each skill below. At the end of each sentence record whether the skill is used for **hunting**, **fishing** or **trapping**.

1. The pioneer would move very quietly through the forest and hide behind trees. _____

2. Using a spear was the best way to catch this type of food. _____

3. The pioneer had to know the routes the animals regularly traveled. _____

4. The pioneer had to have good eyesight and an accurate aim, and be able to throw a spear quickly. _____

5. The pioneer would scrape and tan the hides and furs. _____

6. The pioneer had to aim carefully and use only one shot. _____

7. Lanterns were used to hunt for these animals. _____

8. The pioneer knew how to clean the dead animal and to hide the meat in a safe place. _____

9. During the winter, snowshoes were used to travel over the snow while doing this activity. _____

10. The pioneer needed to have good balance or he would end up with a cold, wet surprise. _____

11. The pioneer would be wrapped warmly while he sat and waited. _____

12. The pioneer used snares, deadfalls and pit traps to catch animals. _____

13. The pioneer looked for animal tracks on the ground. _____

Pioneer Clothing

Pioneers could not go to a store to buy new clothes whenever they were needed. They made their own clothes, even the material for them as well.

Shearing the Sheep

In June, on a pioneer farm, the family gathered in the barn to help wash the sheep so their *fleece* would be clean before they were sheared. A few days later, the sheep were rounded up and returned to the barn to be sheared this time. It took two people to shear each sheep. One person held the animal still, while the other person used *clipping shears* to remove the fleece. Sheep look rather small and naked once they have been sheared and usually leave the barn bleating loudly.

The fleece was then spread out on the barn floor and all the dirty edges were snipped away. The wool from the fleece was matted and tangled and had to be combed before it was spun into thread.

Carding the Wool

The process of combing and brushing the wool is called *"carding"* and it is completed with *wooden paddles* called *"carders"* that are covered with wire teeth. A handful of wool is placed on one carder while the other carder is drawn across it, untangling the matted and twisted fibres. This method is similar to the way you brush long hair to remove snarls and tats. This action is repeated several times until all the fibres are straight and no longer tangled. The wool is removed from the carder by drawing one carder backwards making a roll of untangled wool. This piece of wool is called a *"sliver"*. The slivers are stored in a basket to be spun later into thread.

Spinning the Wool

Spinning wool is simply pulling and twisting the fibres. The slivers are spun into a thread using a *"drop spindle"* that is attached to a large wheel called a *"walking wheel"*. The spinner turns the wheel with her hand or a stick. Then the spinner walks back and forth. As the spinner walks away the revolving wheel twists the thread. As she walks back the thread winds on the *"bobbin"*. The bobbin, usually a dried corncob, was placed over the spindle. A spinner would walk many kilometres each day while she was spinning the wool.

45

Pioneer Clothing

Some pioneer women used the "Scottish wheel" for spinning the wool. This was a much smaller wheel and the spinner was able to sit down to spin. A "foot treadle" was used to operate the wheel. It also had a "removable bobbin". Spinning was easier and faster using this wheel. "Flax" could also be spun into linen thread on it as well. The filled bobbins were stored in baskets and waited to be wound on a device called a "niddy noddy" or a "winder" by a family member.

Some pioneers grew a grass-like plant called "flax". The stalks of the plant were soaked and beaten and then the fibres were spun into a fine thread called "linen" and a coarse thread called "tow".

Dyeing the Wool

When all the spinning was finished, it was time to dye the wool before it could be woven into cloth. Early pioneers often lived a drab, dreary existence so they tried to brighten their world by using bright dyes to make their clothing and bedding colourful. Some pioneers bought dyes at the general store but they were usually expensive, so they were only used for special items such as a bed coverlet. Herbal dyes were used mainly for clothing.

Throughout the summer the women of the family hunted for flowers, leaves, berries and bark to dye their wool. A brown dye was made from tea or crushed walnut shells. This was a popular colour for everyday clothes as it didn't show the dirt. Logwood chips were used to make black dye. Goldenrod blossoms and onion skins made a soft, yellow dye. The flowers from Queen Anne's lace made a soft, green; blueberries, a washed out blue; sumac, orange; marigolds, orange and yellow; lily-of-the-valley, green-gold; balm blossoms, pink; blackberries, purple; bloodroot, deep red; and the roots of the madder plant produced a rusty red dye.

Many flowerheads were required to make the dye to colour the yarn. They were boiled until the colour was the way the dyer wanted it. The skeins of wool were dropped into the pots of dye and simmered for a while. The skeins were then simmered in a "mordant" to set the colour so it would not wash out or fade. The early pioneers had to use "urine" as a mordant. The acid in the urine made the colours permanent. The coloured skeins of wool were then stored in cedar baskets to keep them safe from moths.

Pioneer Clothing

Weaving the Thread

Some pioneer women had their own looms to weave their wool into cloth. Most women took their wool to a local weaver in town to have it done. The weaver would show the pioneer woman the patterns he could weave and she would choose one.

Weaving requires skill and energy. A good weaver could make 2.7 metres (3 yards) of 76 centimetre (30 inch) wide cloth in a day. The weaver was paid with the extra skeins of wool. These skeins were used to make cloth for his family or to sell to the local general store.

The pioneer women used the wool to knit socks, hats, mitts, scarves and long underwear to keep out the winter cold. The yarn was also knitted into blankets, chair covers and curtains for the house. Carpets were made by pulling pieces of yarn through a backing of heavy burlap with a special needle. This was called rug hooking.

Evenings, during pioneer times, were busy ones for women and their daughters. They sewed and mended clothes by the light of the fire or a candle. Holes and tears were mended with the fabric from worn out clothes. Every scrap of material was saved to make patchwork quilts. Braided or rag rugs were made from cloth that was too worn to use for quilts. The women also made lace to decorate bedsheets, tablecloths and pillow cases.

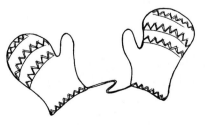
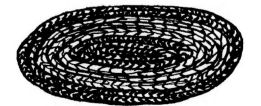

SSF1-06

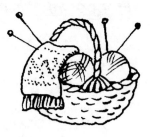

Pioneer Reading Activity Fourteen

Read the Information cards entitled *"Pioneer Clothing"*.

Making cloth for clothing and quilts was a long and tedious task for a pioneer woman. Many steps were taken.

Number the steps in the correct order in the sentences below.

From Fleece to Cloth

_____ The slivers of wool were stored in a basket.

_____ The pioneer women spent days, during the summer, searching for flowers, leaves, berries and bark to use for dyes to color their wool.

_____ The sheep were gathered in the barn to have their fleece washed.

_____ The thread on the bobbins was later wound on a device called a "niddy noddy" or a "winder" by a family member.

_____ A few days later the sheep were taken to the barn to be sheared.

_____ The plants were boiled in a large kettle until the liquid was the right color.

_____ The wool was woven into cloth on a loom by the pioneer woman or the wool was taken to a weaver in town.

_____ The skeins of wool were dipped into kettles of dye and simmered for a while.

_____ The slivers were spun into a fine thread using a walking wheel or a Scottish wheel and wound onto bobbins.

_____ The wool was then brushed with carders to untangle the matted and tangled fibres.

_____ The skeins were next simmered in a "mordant" to set the color so it would not fade or wash out.

_____ The dirty edges on the fleece were cut away.

_____ The colored skeins of wool were then stored in cedar baskets to be used later.

Traveling in Pioneer Days

Early pioneers traveled in a variety of ways to get from one place to another. They traveled by sailing ships to reach North America where they would make a new home. After a stormy ocean voyage, most new settlers had to travel inland by boat and by covered wagon or by foot to their new homestead.

Pioneers usually made their homesteads near rivers or lakes so they could travel to the closest village, gristmill, general store and church by boat. *"Birchbark canoes"* and *"dugouts"* were the first boats used by the pioneers. Canoes were light and could be carried overland easily.

Later people used *"bateaux"*, *"flatboats"*, *"rafts"*, *"sailboats"*, *"horseboats"*, and *"keelboats"* for travel. *"Steamboats"* eventually made water travel much faster and more efficient.

The building of *"canals"* improved water travel immensely. Canals were built to detour boats around rapids or to link up bodies of water such as lakes and rivers. Travelers no longer had to portage or carry their boats around rapids or from a lake to a river.

In the early days, traveling by land was much more difficult as there were no roads. People who did not have horses or wagons had to walk to town for their supplies. They relied on trails made by the Native People through forests. Trees were chipped or *"blazed"* with a hatchet. These marked trails were called "blazed trails".

In time, groups of pioneers got together to build rough *roads*. Trees were chopped down on each side of the trail. The trails were wider but the roads were bumpy and full of stumps. In the spring and summer the roads were often muddy and horses and wagons often became stuck in the wet, swampy ground.

In order to solve the mud problem, the settlers cut the trees that were chopped down around the trails into logs. The logs were split in half and laid flat-side down close to each other on the road. These roads were called *"corduroy roads"* after a ribbed fabric. These roads were often dangerous. Horses were terrified of them and frequently refused to travel over them. Horses sometimes broke their legs when they slipped into the spaces between two logs or they easily tripped. Sometimes, wagons lost wheels or were wrecked on these roads.

Pioneer Transportation

"*Plank roads*" replaced the corduroy roads. Logs were cut into planks or boards and laid side by side on the mud. These roads were less bumpy and much safer. Each farmer built a road in front of his or her house. Sometimes larger groups built a fine network of roads for the entire community.

Once roads began to appear, *bridges* over rivers and streams had to be constructed. They were made of wood or stone. Some of the bridges were completely covered and used as a place to stay out of bad rainstorms and blizzards.

Animals such as *horses* and *oxen* were very important to the

early pioneer. They were used to pull *carts, wagons, carriages* and *sleighs* of all sorts. Horses were often ridden to get from one place to the other. *Stagecoaches* carried travelers, supplies and the mail. They traveled from town to town and stopped to change horses every 24 kilometres (14 miles), to let people off and to deliver the mail and supplies. The arrival of the stagecoach was announced by the coach driver blowing a horn. During the winter the coaches were changed into sleighs. A *stagewagon* was similar to a farmer's wagon. It was used for shorter trips and on back roads. Stagecoaches were used for longer trips. Traveling by stagecoach was bumpy, uncomfortable and dusty. The travelers slept in inns and hotels at night during the trip.

When the *railroad* began to open up the west, many new settlers came. The railroad enabled small communities to get supplies from larger towns in good time. People could travel farther, more quickly and in better comfort than on a stagecoach. Traveling by train was the fastest way but not always the safest. Trains often were derailed or collided with one another.

Pioneer Reading Activity Fifteen

Read the Information Cards entitled *"Traveling in Pioneer Days"*.

Answer each question with a complete sentence.

1. What types of boats did the pioneer use in the beginning?

   _____

   _____

2. Why were canals built in pioneer days?

   _____

   _____

3. What are "blazed" trails and who made them?

   _____

   _____

4. What were the first pioneer roads like?

   _____

   _____

5. What is a "corduroy road" and how was it made?

   _____

   _____

6. Why were "corduroy roads" dangerous?

   _____

   _____

7. Why were "plank roads" better than "corduroy roads"?

   _____

   _____

8. What did the pioneers have to build in order to cross rivers and streams?

   _____

   _____

9. How were animals such as horses and oxen important to the pioneer?

   _____

   _____

10. Why was the stagecoach an important method of transportation?

   _____

   _____

Early Pioneer Children

Pioneer children led much different lives from the lives of children today. Parents felt children needed to learn right from wrong at a very early age. There was no time for fun, playing or laziness. They took their duties as parents very seriously. Their children were to be *well-behaved, quiet* and *obedient.* Parents needed their children to be hard-workers. Children were treated like *"little adults"* and were often dressed like adults as well.

In pioneer days boys and girls were treated differently. A pioneer father taught his sons how to do chores in the fields and the barns while the pioneer mother taught her daughters chores to do in the house such as cooking, sewing, knitting, quilting, cleaning, making candles, and many other things.

Pioneer children were taught that *laziness* was the worst sin of all. They had to get up early in the morning and do chores before going to school. After school they had to hurry home to do chores before supper. Children were *punished* if they complained or said they were tired.

Boys and girls both learned to sew and knit. Boys learned to sew simple stitches while girls learned to make many different types of stitches. Boys and girls picked berries, fed the animals, gathered fruit and vegetables, dipped candles, collected eggs, churned butter and brought in the kindling and firewood.

The women and girls were responsible for most of the work inside the home. At a very young age, girls were taught to spin, weave, make candles and soap, sew, bake bread, make butter and cheese, and cook. Pioneer girls also had to clean the house and wash the dishes.

Pioneer children wore simple clothing that lasted a long time. Dresses for girls were made of linen or wool. Often linen and wool were woven together to make a sturdy fabric called "linsey-woolsey". Skirts were loose and long and reached to the ankles. A pinafore, a long apron, protected a girl's dress from stains.

       SSF1-06

Pioneer Children

Pioneer boys wore long cotton shirts and woollen or linen pants. Sometimes a short jacket was worn over the shirt and pants. In some areas, boys wore "buckskin" shirts, breeches (pants) and jackets.

Each child usually had one pair of shoes to wear but were encouraged to go barefoot most of the time. New shoes were expensive and the one pair had to last a long time. Shoes were passed down from the oldest child to the youngest one if they were still in good condition. Some children wore buckskin moccasins in the dry weather.

Toys in pioneer days were simple and home-made. The children had very few toys to play with. Many dolls and animals were whittled out of wood by a grandfather or the father during the winter months. Dolls were also made out of corn husks. Sometimes children played with a simple hoop and a stick. The child would roll the hoop and try to keep it going by pushing it with the stick. Girls liked to use a piece of rope for skipping and sang many rhymes and jingles while they played. In the winter, pioneer children would go sledding, tobogganing, snowshoeing and skating. In the summer, they enjoyed swimming, fishing and playing outside games. One of their favorite games was called the "Fox and the Geese".

"Parlor games" were played indoors by pioneer children and their parents. They played games such as "Blindman's Bluff", "Pin the Tail on the Donkey", board games and shadow games. While they played, pioneer children had to use their imaginations much more than children of today. They loved to role play and pretend to be mothers and fathers, blacksmiths, storekeepers, doctors and patients. They used things in their environment to create a setting for their playtime activities.

SSF1-06

Pioneer Reading Activity Sixteen

Read the Information Cards entitled *"Early Pioneer Children"*.

Pioneer children had to work very hard. They had many chores to do each day. Some they did together and some they did separately.

Classify the following descriptions according to the headings. **Record** the correct heading on the line after each statement.

Pioneer Boys	**Pioneer Girls**	**Pioneer Boys and Girls**

1. did chores in the fields and the barn _____
2. had to be well-behaved, quiet and obedient _____
3. wore linen or wool dresses covered with a pinafore _____
4. picked berries in the woods _____
5. were taught to spin, weave and sew _____
6. churned butter and collected eggs _____
7. wore trousers and long shirts made of wool or linen _____
8. learned to sew simple stitches _____
9. learned to sew many stitches _____
10. learned to sew and knit _____
11. learned to make and bake bread _____
12. wore buckskin shirts, breeches and jackets _____
13. had simple home-made toys _____
14. played with cornhusk dolls _____
15. learned to make soap and candles _____
16. worked mainly with their fathers _____
17. worked mainly with their mothers _____
18. only had one pair of shoes _____
19. learned to cook, clean the house and wash the dishes _____
20. like to skip with a piece of rope _____

Pioneer Village Life

When the pioneers first came to North America they had to make everything that they needed. Gradually as more and more people came to settle, some decided to set up *"General Stores"* in areas where the people had to travel long distances to buy their supplies. The *"General Store"* opened a whole new life for the pioneers. Separated farms became a community. People were brought together to help each other. The pioneers now had contact with the world they left behind.

Villages grew around the *"General Store"*. The pioneer farmers needed many things done for them. Pioneers who were not farmers set up shops to provide services the pioneers needed. The *"General Store"* was the *"hub"* or center of activity in an early village. Clothes, tools, food items, cloth, china and other products that came from Europe could be bought at the store.

The pioneers picked up their mail at the *"General Store"*. The *"Post Office"* was usually found at the back of the store. Each family had a separate *"cubby hole"* into which the storekeeper put incoming mail. The mail came by stagecoach every two weeks. Outgoing mail was taken away by the stagecoach.

The *"General Store"* was the meeting place in the community. People often sat on a bench outside the store or they gathered around the pot-bellied stove in the winter. The villagers sat around, discussed any news or problems and played cards or checkers. Every Saturday night the store was filled with shoppers. This was a big event for the pioneer women and children as they seldom saw anyone or talked to anyone other than their family members during the week.

The *"General Store"* was usually a two-storey building built in the center of the village or at a crossroads. The store would have two large display windows with a door in the middle. One window would be decorated with hats, dry goods (material), scissors, buttons and things women liked. The other window would display tools and shoes for men. Sometimes awnings were put over the windows to prevent the sun from fading the articles. The awnings also provided a shady spot for the villagers to sit and chat. Most *"General Stores"* had a platform or wooden sidewalk at the front. This made it easier for the farmer to load and unload things. Hitching posts were found on either side of the platform. Horses and wagons were tied to the posts.

"General Stores" always looked cluttered on the inside. Everything the storekeeper had to sell was put on display. Pickles, tobacco, crackers, vinegar and molasses were stored in barrels. Built-in bins held coffee, tea, peas, rice, dried

Pioneer Village Life

fruit and oatmeal. Small drawers held special spices such as pepper, cinnamon, and cloves. Treats such as licorice sticks, stick candy and wax gums were found in tin-covered glass containers on the store counters. The shelves behind the counter were filled with china, glassware and silverware. On the counter stood large brass scales to weigh many of the items to be sold. No space was wasted in a "General Store" and things such as lamps, lanterns, pails and tools were hung from the ceiling.

The *"storekeeper"* had to be many people all rolled into one. He was the politician chosen by the people because he knew everyone in the community. He had to be a good businessman and buy and trade goods fairly with the settlers. The *"storekeeper"* had to be good in mathematics in order to keep his books and accounts in order. People depended on him to know about laws and how they worked. He was the news-bringer for the community and brought back all the news he had learned about what was happening in the country and new products, fashion ideas and new ways of doing things. He had to be friendly and to be careful not to offend his customers.

The early pioneers often traded items the *"storekeeper"* needed for things that they needed. Very little money was exchanged during early pioneer times. The pioneers would trade flour, pork, butter, honey, beef, eggs, chickens, ducks, geese, hides, fruit, syrup, wool, goose feathers, soap and cider for sugar, spices, dried fruits, molasses, rum, iron goods, drugs, china, gun powder, silk, satin, dye, rice, tea, buttons and coffee.

As the pioneer community grew in size, so did the village. More skilled tradesmen came to set up their stores and shops. The "gristmill was one of the first buildings to be built in a village. It was usually located near water which was used to operate the grindstones. The "miller" ground wheat, corn, rye and oat grains into different types of flour for the pioneer.

         SSF1-06

Pioneer Village Life

A "sawmill" was another business that was needed in the community because everything the pioneers made was mainly made of wood. They needed the wood to build their homes, barns, storage bins, barrels, buckets and furniture, to name a few. The "sawmill" was also built near water. It used the energy that water provided just like the gristmill. A *waterwheel* turned, creating the power to saw logs into "planks". Using planks, the settlers could build two-storey houses that had many rooms with wooden floors.

The sawmill in the village brought other craftsmen such as "carpenters", "coopers" and "wheelwrights" to the community. Carpenters built houses, tables, chairs and cabinets. They knew every type of wood and how to use it. "Coopers" made buckets, barrels and tubs. Wooden containers were used to store almost everything. A pioneer community needed hundreds of barrels so the cooper was a busy person. "Wheelwrights" made wheels and "wainwrights" made wagons. Both wagons and wheels had to be constantly repaired because the roads were bumpy and rough.

The "blacksmith" was usually the first metalworker to open shop in a pioneer village. He made many things out of black iron hence the name of "blacksmith". The blacksmith made fireplace tools and cooking utensils for the pioneer home. He made hoops for the cooper's barrels and iron rims for the wheelwright's wheels. The carpenter depended on the blacksmith for nails, latches and hinges. The farmer needed him to make farming equipment. A special blacksmith called a "farrier" made horseshoes for oxen and horses and nailed the shoes onto the hooves of the animals.

The "pewterer", "silversmith" and "tinsmith" created many useful and decorative items for the pioneer home. The *pewterer* and *silversmith* made shoe buckles, buttons, candlesticks, dishes, spoons, cups and teapots, etc. The *tinsmith* used tin to make such things as pails, lanterns and kitchen utensils.

As the village grew larger, other craftsmen such as the "saddle and harness makers", "printers", "bakers", "cobblers" (shoemakers), "weavers", "gunsmiths", "broom-makers" and "dressmakers" set up shops. In time a one room schoolhouse was built to be used as a school and church. Later on a church was built which became the social center for many events.

Pioneer Reading Activity Seventeen

Read the Information Cards entitled *"Pioneer Village Life"*.

The pioneer village grew larger as the community around it grew. Many shops and craftsmen helped the early pioneers.

Match the name of the shop or craftsman to the service it/he/she provided.
Record the answer on the line at the end of each description.

storekeeper	carpenter	blacksmith	miller	cooper
pewterer	sawmill	wheelwright	silversmith	gristmill
wainwright	tinsmith	saddle maker	gunsmith	weaver
harness maker	dressmaker	cobbler	farrier	teacher
General Store	minister	baker	printer	broom-maker

1. ground wheat, corn, rye and oat grains into different types of flour _____

2. the hub or center of activity in a pioneer village _____

3. wooden planks were made here _____

4. built houses, tables, chairs and cabinets _____

5. made things for the pioneer's home and farm out of black metal _____

6. made and repaired rifles and shotguns _____

7. made horseshoes for the horses and oxen and nailed them on _____

8. made fancy candlesticks, plates and teapots (two answers) _____
   _____

9. used tin to make pails, lanterns and kitchen utensils _____

10. made shoes and boots _____

11. made many barrels, buckets and tubs _____

12. repaired and made wagon wheels _____

13. built and repaired wagons for the pioneers _____

14. provided the pioneers with the many things that they needed _____

15. made dresses and cloaks for the pioneer women _____

Early Pioneer Schools

When the pioneers first settled in North America, many of them taught their children life skills and how to survive in this new land. There was very little time given to *"book-learning"* as there was too much work to be done and there were no schools available. Some parents did teach their children to read and write.

As the pioneers became more settled in an area, the parents would decide that it was time for their children to go to school. The pioneer community would work together and build a one-room schoolhouse similar to a log house. The school often had a dirt floor. The windows were covered with greased paper instead of glass which allowed light to come in.

The children sat on backless benches at narrow tables that faced the walls because the table tops were built into them. Some schools were heated with a fireplace or a box wood stove. The heat was not spread out evenly throughout the room. Those who sat close to the fire were too hot while those who sat far from it froze. One student was given the job of starting the fire each cold morning. This had to be done well before the other children arrived so the school would be warm.

The children often had to walk through woods and along early roads for nine to ten kilometres (five to six miles) to attend classes at the school. School was often held six days a week.

The parents would advertise for a teacher. The parents paid the teacher's salary and supplied the school with wood. Each family paid the teacher twenty-five cents for every child attending school each month. So if a family had three children attending school, it paid the teacher seventy-five cents each month. Very few teachers wanted to teach school in the backwoods as the pay was very low and the money was often difficult to collect.

Sometimes the teacher was paid with bags of grain or food that he would have to sell for money. There were times when the teacher had to board with each family for a month at a time. Working at a backwoods school was a difficult and rough task and men

Early Pioneer Schools

were usually hired to be teachers. Sometimes the teenage boys would lock the teacher out of the school or play tricks on him. Sometimes they would pick a fight with the teacher, so the teacher had to be physically strong enough to defend himself.

Teachers were very strict and ruled with a stick and a very sharp, nasty tongue. Students were often beaten for anything from not knowing their work to being late for school. Parents seldom complained about this treatment as they believed that if you "spare the rod", you will "spoil the child".

The schools could not afford to buy books or paper for the students. The teacher may have had his own speller and Bible. The first reader that pioneer children usually read was the Bible. Most pioneer families had their own. If a family could afford to buy a reader, it would be passed down from the oldest child to the youngest child in the family.

Learning the letters of the alphabet and numbers were the first things pioneer children were taught. They practiced the letters of the alphabet on slates with slate pencils or chalk as well as their "sums". Later the letters were practiced on paper with quill pens and home-made ink that was brought from home.

The one-room school was not the best way for children to learn. The school was closed for part of the year because the students who lived on farms stayed home to help with the planting and harvesting. The teacher found it difficult to teach so many grades at one time. Older students soon knew all that the teacher could teach them. The desks were not built to accommodate the students' different sizes. The students were taught to memorize and to recite everything they learned. During art classes, the students could only draw the things the teacher wanted. The only exercise the children received was marching to and from their desks. There were no gym classes in those days. Children were harshly punished. They would have to stand in corners, wear dunce caps, balance blocks of woods or wear signs tied around their necks. Many students received the strap.

Pioneer Reading Activity Eighteen

Read the Information Cards entitled *"Pioneer Schools"*.

Locate the sentence in the information that proves each statement below is true. **Record** the first **five** words of the sentence on the line at the end of each statement.

1. Pioneer children had to walk much farther to school than children of today.

   _____

2. The schoolhouse was built by the community.

   _____

3. The school was poorly heated and very uncomfortable to learn in.

   _____

4. The teacher's salary was paid by the parents.

   _____

5. The school teachers were mainly men.

   _____

6. Teachers in pioneer times were not very kind to their pupils.

   _____

7. The desks were very uncomfortable for the students to sit at and work.

   _____

8. The children did not have materials for reading and writing.

   _____

9. Most pioneer children learned to read the Bible first.

   _____

10. The students did not have paper and pencils to practice the letters and their sums.

   _____

11. Children were often beaten by the teacher for any reason.

   _____

12. The pioneers taught their children how to survive.

   _____

Pioneer Health and Medicines

It is amazing that the early pioneers survived as well as they did without doctors and medicines. Mother Nature was very kind to them and on their side. In those days there was plenty of fresh air and the sun shone brightly. There were no factories or cars and so no smog or polluted air. The pioneers were in good physical condition as they walked long distances and worked extremely hard building their homes and homesteads. There were no chemical preservatives in their food. They were able to use trees, roots and plants found on their farms to cure minor illnesses.

Early pioneers did not know about germs and how they were spread. They did not know that *cleanliness* was important in preventing *diseases*. They did not know *germs* thrive in unclean places. Animals such as rats and mice often carried germs while on sailing ships.

Many settlers did not eat nutritious meals. They were not able to get a variety of fruits and vegetables, meat, dairy products and grains at all times of the year. During the winter, pioneers lived on a diet of meat, potatoes and bread. They lacked important vitamins such as Vitamin C.

Settlers often became ill in the winter with a disease called *"scurvy"*. This disease is caused by a lack of Vitamin C which is found in fresh fruits. Scurvy causes the gums to swell and become bloody. The pioneers' teeth fell out and they felt extremely tired, got sores on their arms and legs and their muscles swelled.

Milk is an important part of a good diet especially for children who are growing. In pioneer times, milk was dangerous to drink. It contained germs that caused diseases such as scarlet fever, typhoid fever, diptheria and a type of tuberculosis that damaged children's bones and joints. Milk was not *"pasteurized"* in the early days. Pasteurizing milk is the process of heating milk to just below its boiling point. This process kills the bacteria (germs) in the milk.

Many diseases had the same symptoms of fever, vomiting, headaches and coughing. Doctors had problems diagnosing the various diseases. Pioneer people often suffered from a disease called *"ague"* which we call the *"flu"* today. *"Pneumonia"* is a disease of the lungs caused by a bad cold often suffered by the pioneers. Pioneer children suffered childhood diseases such as *mumps, measles, chicken pox, scarlet fever, whooping cough, polio and diptheria.* Many of these diseases are controlled today by vaccination.

The pioneers were often threatened by *"epidemic"* diseases. Epidemic diseases were highly contagious and spread rapidly from person to person. One of the most

Pioneer Health and Medicines

dreaded epidemic diseases was *"cholera"*. The victims of cholera suffered from nausea, vomiting, chills, thirst and spasms. Many pioneers died from this disease. Cholera epidemics were frequently brought by the ships filled with new settlers. The ships were often unclean and crowded and many of the new settlers were suffering from cholera. These new settlers had to be confined to a hospital and *"quarantined"* or isolated from everyone.

"Tuberculosis" was another disease, called *"consumption"* by the pioneers. This disease damaged and destroyed organs in the body resulting in death. It was a highly contagious disease and people with this disease were sent to *"sanatoriums"* for rest, good food and fresh air.

Early doctors learned about medicine working for other doctors. This learning period was called an *"apprenticeship"*. Young apprentices had many duties to do such as caring for the doctor's horse, sweeping the office, running errands, delivering messages, mixing plasters, and gathering herbs. An apprentice, after working for a doctor for years as his servant, eventually called himself a doctor. He did not have to attend school for a long period of time, write difficult exams or need a diploma. When the doctor felt his apprentice was ready to work on his own, the apprentice became a doctor.

Doctors often made people feel sicker instead of better. Pioneers did not always trust doctors and doctors often had to work at something else as well in order to make a living. Often the village doctor was the *"apothecary"* (pharmacist) as well. Doctors mixed and gave medicines to their patients. Some medicines were made from herbs while others contained dangerous ingredients such as mercury. Large doses of mercury can cause death. Doctors also used gold, silver, ground pearls and precious stones in their remedies.

The *country doctor* often made house calls and traveled by horse or a horse and buggy, as few people went to his office. The doctor was a friend to all his patients. He delivered many of the babies and watched them grow up. The country doctor stayed with his patient for as long as he was needed. Few pioneers could afford to pay the doctor in money, so he was paid with chicken, meat, eggs, vegetables or grain.

Very few doctors today make house calls. Instead we must travel to the doctor's office or clinic. Unfortunately we do not get to know our doctor very well.

Pioneer Reading Activity Nineteen

Read the Information Card entitled
"Pioneer Health and Medicines".

Complete the following activities.

A) List **five** good reasons why the pioneers were able to survive without doctors and medicines.

1. _____

_____

2. _____

_____

3. _____

_____

4. _____

_____

5. _____

_____

B) List **five** ways germs were spread in pioneer days.

1. _____

_____

2. _____

_____

3. _____

_____

4. _____

_____

5. _____

_____

C) **List** the names of the various pioneer diseases. **Star** the ones that make people sick today in North America.

_____

_____

How the Native People Helped the Early Pioneers

Without the knowledge and help of the Native People living in North America, many of the settlers would not have survived their first difficult years establishing their homesteads.

Did you know that the Native People taught the early pioneers the following skills?

- Wooden bowls were made from maple burls. A burl is a growth on the side of the tree. It is naturally shaped like a bowl. The Native People taught the pioneers how to hollow out and polish burls. The maple burl has a tight grain and does not crack easily.

- The pioneers were shown how to use fire to hollow out logs. Hollowed out logs were used as buckets for carrying water.

- The Native People taught them to use green hardwood to make hooks for their cooking pots that hung over the fire.

- They were taught to plant crops that grow well in the new land such as corn, pumpkins and squash.

- The Native People showed the pioneers how to fertilize their corn by placing a fish in the hole first with the corn seeds.

- The Native People showed the early pioneers how to tap the maple trees, how to collect the sap and how to boil it over an open fire until the sap became a thick syrup. The pioneers also learned that if they boiled the sap long enough it became sugar.

- The Native People showed the pioneers where to look for edible roots and berries and how to cook them.

- The pioneers were shown how to hunt, fish and trap animals by the Native People.

SSF1-06

How the Native People Helped the Early Pioneers

- The Native children taught the pioneer children which wild plants were safe to eat and pick.

- Native People taught the pioneers how to roast corn and how to make popping corn.

- The pioneers were taught how to build birchbark canoes and dugouts by the Native People.

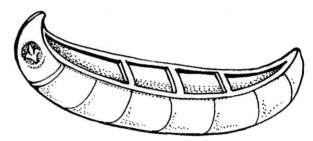

- Many Native guides led explorers and fur trappers to their destinations and taught them many survival skills in this untamed land.

- The Native People taught the settlers how to treat fevers and other minor ailments using plants and herbs in the forests. They told them to chew the inside bark of the willow tree to relieve pain. Today, aspirin is made from this substance.

- The pioneers were shown how to cook meat on an outside spit.

- They were taught how to cook pumpkin and corn and to use them in certain dishes.

- Pioneers and fur trappers were shown how to preserve meat by drying it. They made dried buffalo meat called "pemmican" and carried it with them on long trips. It did not taste very good, but it was easy to carry and was very nourishing.

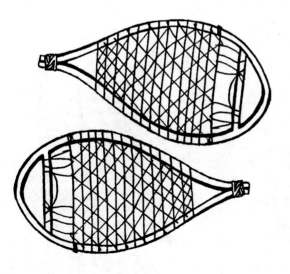

- The Native People taught the settlers how to make and use snowshoes in the winter.

- The pioneers were shown how to make traps, snares and pit-traps to catch animals. They were taught how to read signs and tracks in the forest that helped them track and hunt animals for food.

- The pioneers and trappers were taught how to clean and prepare animal skins and furs to be used for trading purposes.

Pioneer Reading Activity Twenty

Read the Information Card entitled *"How the Native People Helped the Early Pioneers"*.

Record the word **True** or **False** at the end of each sentence below. In each false statement, **underline** the part that is wrong.

1. The Native People showed the pioneers how to make metal hooks to hang their cooking pots on over the fire. _____

2. The pioneers were shown how to hollow out logs by the Native People to make water buckets. _____

3. The pioneers were taught to use beaver meat to fertilize the corn seeds. _____

4. The Native People showed the pioneers where to look for poisonous roots and berries. _____

5. The Native People taught the pioneers how to tap beachnut trees for their sap to make maple syrup. _____

6. Squash, pumpkins, and corn were vegetables the Native People taught the pioneers to grow. _____

7. The pioneers were taught how to fish, hunt, and trap animals. _____

8. The pioneers were taught how to turn a pine burl into a wooden bowl. _____

9. The Native People taught the pioneers how to make pemmican using moose meat. _____

10. The pioneers were shown how to use snowshoes on water. _____

11. The Native People showed the pioneers how to make birchbark canoes. _____

12. The pioneer was able to fish well because he learned how to read signs and tracks in the forest. _____

13. The Native people taught the pioneers how to roast corn and how to make popping corn. _____

14. Native guides taught many explorers and fur trappers how to survive in the wilderness of North America. _____

Alphabetical Order

Pioneer students had to memorize the letters of the alphabet and know their order well.

How well do you know the order of the letters of the alphabet?

In the correct alphabetical order, number the words in the pioneer buckets.

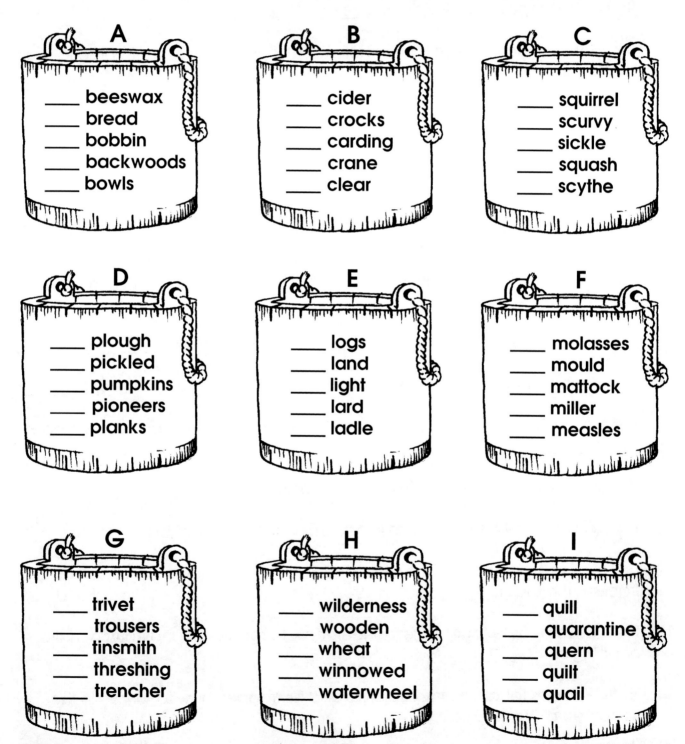

A
____ beeswax
____ bread
____ bobbin
____ backwoods
____ bowls

B
____ cider
____ crocks
____ carding
____ crane
____ clear

C
____ squirrel
____ scurvy
____ sickle
____ squash
____ scythe

D
____ plough
____ pickled
____ pumpkins
____ pioneers
____ planks

E
____ logs
____ land
____ light
____ lard
____ ladle

F
____ molasses
____ mould
____ mattock
____ miller
____ measles

G
____ trivet
____ trousers
____ tinsmith
____ threshing
____ trencher

H
____ wilderness
____ wooden
____ wheat
____ winnowed
____ waterwheel

I
____ quill
____ quarantine
____ quern
____ quilt
____ quail

     SSF1-06

Searching for Pioneer Compound Words

In the word search there are 20 pioneer compound words.

Can you find them all? **Circle** each one that you find.

```
A R U B D N V F O G Z I P I R F U L F E C X
P V G R I S T M I L L U A S Z J W J I W F G
H M Y I O T E Q N P S G Q O K T K V R Y P I
C T Q B W A W J X H F S N O W S H O E S B D
S X K L D G K A D R C H N B L Y D M P A Z V
F A L C G E M Y L B E T Z G E M Q R L O S H
K Z I J E C R A F T S M E N H C I N A U J T
K B M O F O O Q I X L S C U H U K E C C W Z
D T R I N A Y K R W B M T E R F N D E V B K
A L E H Q C P N Z J V A D F G L T M L D B X
S C T P G H O M E M A D E W S S I D M Y I A
M U T E I G R B K X T Y M A T Q J T Q U R N
E Y U H B D J U J S L V Z C O U V O E G C K
Z R B L A C K S M I T H A Z R W Z S O L H P
N X P F C Q I A V K C L Y B E Y R X H T B P
V O G W K H Q W J B X D M G K V V Y C Q F A J
U S T S W P R M O A W N F E E A Z C M I R O
R C D Q O L T I C R G L C M E X W F R N K S
C H H K O R N L B R B I N J P A B B D E H G
B O P I D M S L J E D I K B E E S W A X K R
O O A Z S N A Z H L H A E C R P U A M C Q J
Q L J J K R U G Y M O Y Q K B R Q T B L I O
E H F Y P O O I D A W D I R L A O E N K D P
S O L M W S E X K K X X P Z G N Y R G R S H
G U V I X E W F L E E W F J Z F S W A A H I
H S H O E M A K E R G H Y S E T V H F B E G
U E T N V A M I O V M T Q P M W X E Z H F T
W E B U C R J P H N U R O V P I Z E Y C D J
O V Y K N Y Q P A D D L E W H E E L E R U M
X M S A R D R F G Z X S B H U L V B X I W K
P Z L T Q S E T U W A Y T J C K A E C B L V
```

69

SSF1-06

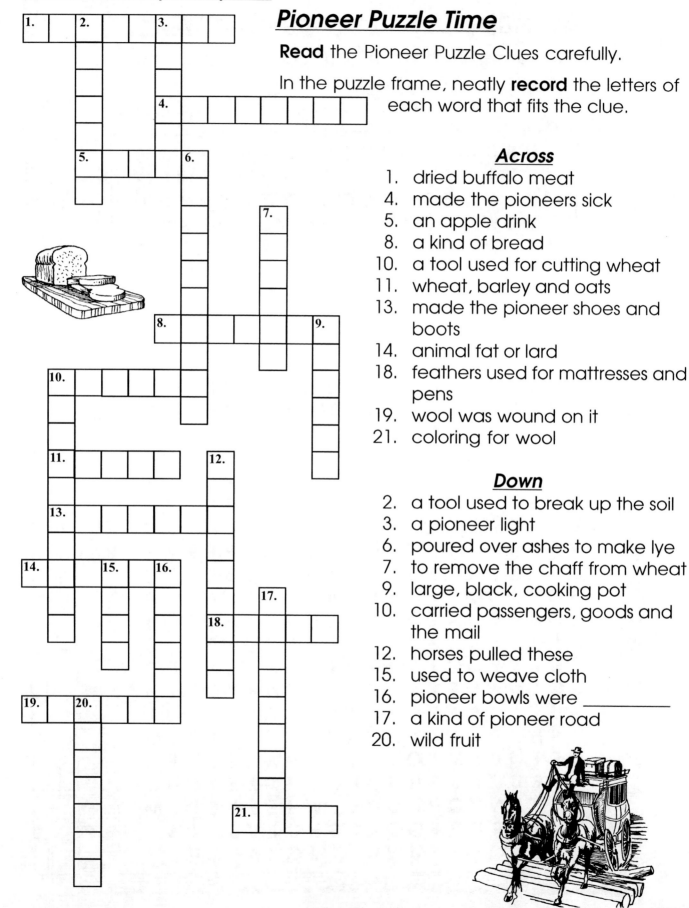

Pioneer Puzzle Time

Read the Pioneer Puzzle Clues carefully.

In the puzzle frame, neatly **record** the letters of each word that fits the clue.

Across

1. dried buffalo meat
4. made the pioneers sick
5. an apple drink
8. a kind of bread
10. a tool used for cutting wheat
11. wheat, barley and oats
13. made the pioneer shoes and boots
14. animal fat or lard
18. feathers used for mattresses and pens
19. wool was wound on it
21. coloring for wool

Down

2. a tool used to break up the soil
3. a pioneer light
6. poured over ashes to make lye
7. to remove the chaff from wheat
9. large, black, cooking pot
10. carried passengers, goods and the mail
12. horses pulled these
15. used to weave cloth
16. pioneer bowls were _____
17. a kind of pioneer road
20. wild fruit

Settler Syllables

Pioneer words may have one, two, three or four syllables.

Classify the pioneer words found in the box according to the number of syllables that you hear in each one.

Record each word in the correct kettle.

lye	petticoat	trencher	flail
kettle	destination	apprenticeship	broadcasting
caldron	persecuted	molasses	scythe
kerosene	pestle	epidemic	yoke

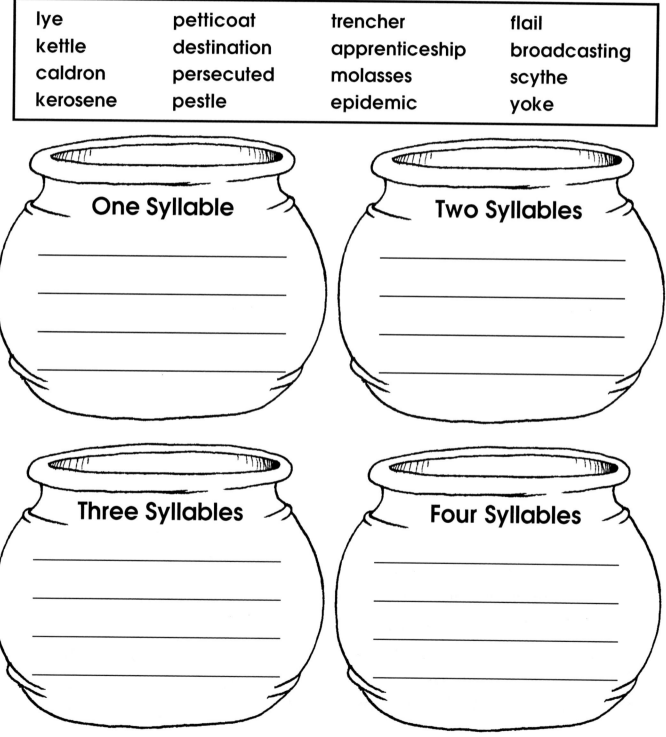

One Syllable

Two Syllables

Three Syllables

Four Syllables

Homonym Hardships

Sometimes using the correct homonym can be a hardship for students.

Homonyms are words that sound the same but have different spellings and meanings. Using the correct one can be difficult.

On the line in each sentence below, **record** the correct homonym, found in the parenthesis.

1. Sarah's father loaded the sacks of wheat in the wagon and took them to the gristmill to be ground into _____. (**flower, flour**)

2. Many settlers _____ on the ship and were buried at _____. (**dyed, died**) (**see, sea**)

3. Each pioneer child only had one _____ of shoes or boots to wear. (**pear, pair, pare**)

4. Ben watched his mother _____ the bread _____ on the table. (**need, knead**) (**dough, doe**)

5. Pioneer children enjoyed looking for _____ in the woods because they _____ them while they picked. (**berries, buries**) (**ate, eight**)

6. Pioneer children went _____ foot in the summer to save _____ shoes from wearing out. (**bear, bare**) (**there, they're, their**)

7. _____ plants often wound themselves around the cornstalks as they grew. (**Been, Bean**)

8. Hot tallow was often poured into tin _____ . (**molds, moulds**)

9. _____ and tallow are used to make soap. (**Lie, Lye**)

10. The venison from _____ was a kind of _____ often served at a pioneer dinner table. (**deer, dear**) (**meat, meet**)

11. The early pioneers _____ clothes that were _____ and drab in color. (**war, wore**) (**plane, plain**)

12. Many pioneer teachers _____ their students for not knowing the work that was taught. (**beet, beat**)

13. Apples were _____ with a special machine. (**pealed, peeled**)

14. In the winter, the pioneers _____ to the village in a _____ pulled by horses. (**road, rode**) (**slay, sleigh**)

Deadly Doubles

Some words have double consonants in the middle or at the end. They often make words difficult to spell.

Complete the words below in the sentences with the correct **pair of double consonants** from the box. Each pair may be used more than once.

ll mm tt bb zz pp ff dd rr nn gg

1. Pioneers bored a hole in each maple tree, then ha ____ered in a wooden spile to co _____ ect the sap.

2. The soup in the ke ____ le bu ____ led while the meat in the ski ____ et si ____ led and sna ____ ed in the fireplace.

3. Pe ____ican was a type of food made from dried bu ____ alo meat.

4. Pioneers traveled on the water by pa ____lewheelers and fe____y boats.

5. The gri ____le, tra ____el, ski ____er and ski ____et are all cooking utensils.

6. Di ____, pe ____ermint, ci ____amon and ta ____agon were herbs and spices used to flavour pioneer dishes.

7. Ta ____ ow was animal fat boiled in a big ke ___le to make candles.

8. The mi ____ er, the sa ____le maker, the co ____ler and the po ____ er were craftsmen who had shops in a pioneer vi ____ age.

9. On land, the pioneer traveled in ca ____iages and bu ____ ies.

10. The pioneer woman spent a great deal of time spi ____ ing wool into yarn and then kni ____ ing it into mi ____ ens, socks and scarves.

The "Qu" Sound in Quilt

The word *"quilt"* begins with the sound that *"qu"* makes.
Other words begin with the same sound.
In each quilt block is a clue for a *"qu"* word.
Read the clue and then **record** the "qu"
word on the line.

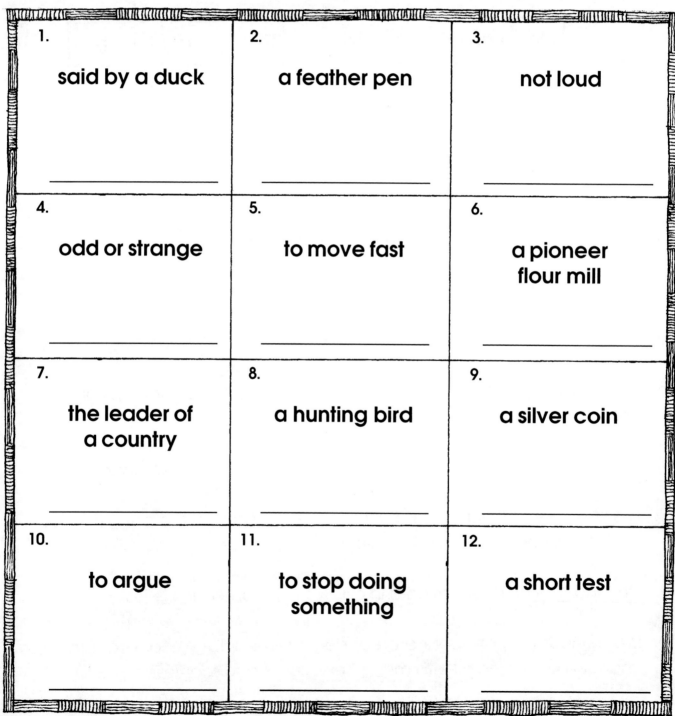

1. said by a duck _____	**2.** a feather pen _____	**3.** not loud _____
4. odd or strange _____	**5.** to move fast _____	**6.** a pioneer flour mill _____
7. the leader of a country _____	**8.** a hunting bird _____	**9.** a silver coin _____
10. to argue _____	**11.** to stop doing something _____	**12.** a short test _____

Sorting Vowel Sounds

Many pioneer words have **long** and **short** vowel sounds that one can hear. **Classify** the words in the box on the correct pioneer vowel slate. **Record** the words neatly.

paddle
kettle
miller
knitting
axes
winder
logging
weaver
Bible
cobbler
stumps
shelter
ague
snare
sums
hoe
cheese
tinsmith
ladle
light
oxen
knead
bush
pork
cradle
use
candle
bowls
community
tent

Long a	Short a
Long e	Short e
Long i	Short i
Long o	Short o
Long u	Short u

Blazing Blanks with Blends

The Native People used to put notches in trees to blaze trails through the forest.

Blaze these sentences by completing each word with the correct missing **blend**.

bl	tw	st	tr	cr	sp	st	sk	cl	sl	fr	pl	dr	gr	sm	fl	br

1. The pioneers _____ aveled to the general _____ ore by ____ eigh in the winter.

2. Sarah's mother cooked the ____ apjacks on the ____ iddle in the fire _____ ace.

3. The _____ack _____ith made _____illets, _____ivets and _____anes out of _____ ack iron.

4. The miller _____ ound wheat, corn, rye and oat _____ ains into different kinds of _____ our.

5. Once the pioneer had _____eared his land of _____ees, _____umps and large _____ones, he _____anted his _____ops.

6. The pioneer used a _____ ough with a sharp _____ade to _____eak up the soil.

7. The pioneers _____ied or boiled meat, or roa _____ ed it on a _____ it.

8. The pioneers _____ied, salted, pickled, _____oked and _____ored food where the weather would not ruin it.

9. The sheep's _____eece was _____ipped from its body with shears and then it was combed and _____ushed.

10. _____ inning wool is pulling and _____isting fibres.

11. The _____ivers of wool are _____ored in ba _____ ets to be _____un later.

12. The _____eins of wool were _____opped into the pots of dye and simmered for a while.

Pioneer Plurals

Plurals are words that mean more than one.

Beside each singular word below **record** its plural form.

1. bush _____   8. dress _____
2. bench _____   9. church _____
3. berry _____   10. stitch _____
4. buggy _____   11. grocery _____
5. scarf _____   12. ferry _____
6. stagecoach _____   13. harness _____
7. goose _____   14. potato _____

Choose **five** of the plural words. **Record** the ones that you chose on the lines below.

_____

_____

Use each plural word in a good pioneer sentence.

1. _____

2. _____

3. _____

4. _____

5. _____

Parlour Phrases

A phrase is a group of words that begins with a preposition.

Example: in the community (where)
on Monday (when)

A phrase can answer the question words:

Who? Why? What? Where? When? How?

Beside each phrase below print the question word that it answers.

Example: on the inside **where**

1. in pioneer days _____
2. in the backwoods _____
3. from cedar logs _____
4. by rebuilding the roof _____
5. in layers _____
6. during the long winter months _____
7. for chinking the walls _____
8. by the Native People _____
9. for glowing embers _____
10. after a threshing bee _____
11. beside the great fireplace _____
12. for sweetening and preserving _____
13. through the woods _____
14. for all pupils _____
15. on long benches _____

Choose **three** of the phrases and use each one in a good sentence.
Underline the phrase you used in each sentence.

1. _____

_____

2. _____

_____

3. _____

_____

Locating Nouns and Verbs

A **noun** is a word that names a person or thing.

Example: churn

A **verb** is an action word. **Example**: chop

In the sentences below **circle** the nouns and **underline** the verbs.

1. Pioneers had to make butter in a wooden churn.

2. Apples were eaten fresh and baked in pies and other desserts.

3. They traded or bartered butter, eggs and vegetables for tools, dishes, cloth,

    coffee, sugar and spices.

4. Once a village had a sawmill, logs could be cut easily into boards.

5. Kerosene is a kind of oil that was burned in lamps for light.

6. Work animals such as horses and oxen pulled wagons and ploughs.

7. A pedlar traveled from village to village selling goods from his wagon.

8. A quilt is a type of blanket made from scraps of colorful fabric.

9. A one-room cabin was made from logs, mud and tree bark.

10. Women tore old cloths into rags and braided them to make rag rugs.

Sweet Sentences

The sentences below are about making maple syrup.

Some are called **statements** because they tell you something.

Some are called **interrogative** sentences because they ask you something.

Others are called **imperative** sentences because they give a command.

Sentences that show excitement or surprise are called **exclamatory** sentences.

Read each sentence below carefully. At the end of each sentence *record* the type of sentence it is.

Statement	Interrogative	Imperative	Exclamatory

1. "Sap's running!" yelled Peter excitedly as he ran out of the sugar bush to the cabin. _____

2. "Get the buckets and spiles." _____

3. Peter and Mr. McGregor bored a hole in each tree, hammered in a spile and placed a bucket at the base of each one. _____

4. What time of year is sap collected to make maple syrup and sugar? _____

5. "Dad!" cried Peter. "Help me! This bucket of sap is too heavy for me to lift!" _____

6. "Watch Peter, you're spilling the sap." _____

7. "How long will it take to boil the sap before it becomes maple syrup?" _____

8. The thick, gooey syrup from the bottom of the kettle was thrown on some clean snow to harden into taffy. _____

On the back of this sheet record **four** different types of sentences.

Punctuating Pioneer Sentences

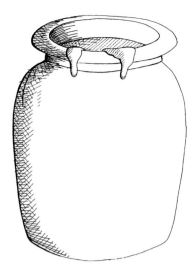

The punctuation marks are missing from the sentences below.

Put in the missing punctuation marks. Use a red pencil crayon.

Remember to use the period (.), the question mark (**?**), the comma (**,**), the exclamation mark (**!**) and quotation marks (" ").

1. Look at what I bought from the pedlar cried Sarah excitedly

2. What color will Martha dye her wool for her new quilt

3. The storekeeper sold cotton fabric buttons thimbles china dishes apple peelers and school supplies

4. What do you have in your crock Sarah asked the storekeeper

5. How much does it cost to mail a letter in pioneer times

6. The pioneer women collected flower heads leaves roots and tree bark to make dye

7. Watch out for the milk cried Meg as she grabbed the bucket from under the cow

8. The family packed warm clothes heavy boots pewter dishes iron pots and frying pans into two large steamer trunks

9. Billy followed the honey bee to a large old maple tree and found a hive full of honey

10. This maple syrup tastes delicious exclaimed Ben as he hungrily ate the stack of steaming flapjacks

11. The pioneers used horses to pull their wagons stagecoaches carriages and buggies

12. I think these tracks are the kind that lynx make said Willie in a frightened voice

Locating Adjectives and Adverbs

An **adjective** is a word that describes a noun.

Example: *dirty* clothes

An **adverb** is a word that describes a verb.

Example: walked *slowly*

In the sentences below **circle** the adjectives and **box** the adverbs.

1. The crackling fire in the fireplace burned merrily during the cold, winter evening.

2. The pioneer mother used her left foot to gently rock the wooden cradle while she peeled potatoes.

3. The flickering candle went out suddenly leaving the room in total darkness.

4. Mary's mother gently kneaded the soft dough so her bread would bake lightly and airily.

5. The warm blackberry pie that was sitting on the table smelled heavenly.

6. The steaming sap that was bubbling steadily over the fire had to be stirred constantly so it would not burn.

7. The delicious smell of licorice sticks and saltwater taffy made Joey's mouth water terribly.

8. The huge waterwheel was slowly turned by the flowing water from the large millpond.

9. The beautiful quilt that decorated Sarah's bed had been stitched neatly and carefully.

10. Hot water slowly dripped through the ashes producing a thick liquid called lye.

Building a House

Compare building a pioneer home to building a modern home.

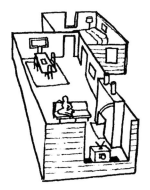

Pioneer Home   **Modern Home**

Pioneer Research Activity Two

Cleaning a House

Compare how a pioneer woman cleaned to the way a modern day woman cleans.

Cleaning a Pioneer Home   **Cleaning a Modern Home**

Pioneer Research Activity Three

Cooking Meals

Compare how a pioneer woman cooked her meals to the way a modern woman cooks.

Pioneer Cooking   **Modern Day Cooking**

Storing and Preserving Food

Compare the ways a pioneer woman stored and preserved her foods with the way a modern day woman does.

Pioneer Woman's Ways   **Modern Woman's Ways**

- -

Washing Clothes

Compare how a pioneer mother washed her family's clothes with the way a modern mother washes her family's clothes.

Pioneer Times   **Modern Times**

- -

Ironing Clothes

Compare how a pioneer mother ironed her family's clothes with the way a modern day woman irons.

Pioneer Times   **Modern Times**

Keeping Clean

Compare the ways that the pioneers kept clean to the ways people of today keep clean.

Pioneer Times

Modern Times

- -

Pioneer Research Activities:

Photocopy the sheet on page 86 and make seven copies. On pages 83, 84, and 85 you will find the headers that are to be glued to the top of the sheet. Each header will be a separate activity for your research center. Photocopy the master activity cards to make the required sheets and place them in file folders that have an example of the activity on the outside.

Example:

Craftsmen Riddles

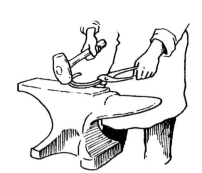

There were many different types of craftsmen who helped the pioneers in many ways.

Choose **one** of the craftsmen from the box below.

miller	blacksmith	pedlar	logger
wheelwright	weaver	storekeeper	wainwright
carpenter	farrier	harness maker	cobbler
tinsmith	silversmith	pewterer	cooper

Make up a **riddle** about the one that you chose.

Write **three** good clues in your riddle.

Record the riddle on a card in your best writing or printing.

On the **back** of the card, write the **name** of the craftsman.

Example:

Front	Back

Front	Back
I work on a loom. I use wool to make cloth. I can put pretty patterns on the cloth. I am a _____.	weaver

Creating a Pioneer Acrostic

An acrostic poem is one that describes one thing. It describes the word that you use. This type of poem does not rhyme.

Choose a pioneer word that you find interesting.

Write the word **vertically** on a piece of paper.

Think of words or phrases that describe the word.

The first word of each line of the poem must begin with each letter of the pioneer word.

Example:

P eople who traveled far

I n small sailing ships

O n the rough Atlantic Ocean

N orth America was their new home

E very pioneer worked hard

E ven the pioneer children

R abbit or raccoon for supper

S erved in a soup or stew

Illustrate your acrostic poem too.

Pioneer Story Time

The pioneers were great story tellers.

They loved to gather around the fireplace on
cold winter nights and tell stories about their experiences.

Pretend that you are a pioneer child telling a story about an experience
that you have had.

Choose one of the following titles and write an exciting pioneer adventure
story.

Fire In the Bush!

First Time Milking a Cow

The Burning Apron

Sleighbells in the Snow

First Day at a Pioneer School

The Day the Pigs Got Out!

Meeting a Wolf in the Forest

A Delicious Spring Treat!

Caught in a Blizzard

My Native Friend

Working the Churn

The Pedlar's Visit

Trouble at School

Granny's Story

Answer Key

Pioneer Reading Activity One: *(page 15)*

1. Explorers from France, England and Spain visited North America first.
2. They were searching for a better route to the West Indies and Asia. They were also looking for gold.
3. **a)** People wanted to own their own home, farm or business.
   b) Europe and the British Isles were overcrowded and farmland was disappearing.
   c) Jobs were hard to find.
   d) There was a potato famine in Ireland and people were losing their homes.
   e) People in England and Germany were being persecuted for their religious beliefs.
4. Travelers were kept in the hold for the entire trip. This area became very dirty and smelly. People had nothing to do. The trip took a long time. Many people became sick and died. The rough waters made the passengers seasick.
5. They are deadly diseases.
6. Scurvy is caused by the lack of fresh fruit and vegetables.

Pioneer Reading Activity Two: *(page 17)*
Part A:

1. A logging bee takes place when all the farmer's neighbours bring their own axes and cut down trees to help clear his land quickly.
2. His wife provides them with food and drink while they work. The farmer helps any of them when they need help.
3. Choppers are men who are hired by the land owner to clear his land for him.

Part B:
4, 1, 6, 2, 5, 3

Pioneer Reading Activity Three: *(page 20)*
1. sod house   2. stone house   3. plank house   4. log house   5. sod house   6. log house
7. plank house   8. sod house   9. log house   10. stone house   11. log house   12. plank house

Pioneer Reading Activity Four: *(page 22)*
1. heart, stove, light, heat   2. built, bricks, clay, water, limestone   3. beds, walls, jack
4. loft, room, trundle   5. hand, wood   6. bake, bricks, heated, embers
7. cabin, small, one, rooms   8. wooden, trenchers, spoons   9. Buckets, barrels, hollowed
10. winter, house, barn   11. furniture, simple, useful   12. wood, tied, pegged

Pioneer Reading Activity Five: *(page 24)*
4, 7, 2, 5, 1, 6, 3

The early pioneer cleared the land of trees, stumps and large rocks. The hard ground was broken up by hand with a hoe, or a plough pulled by oxen was used. A heavy, wooden frame with sharp teeth was drawn across the earth to break up the large clumps of earth. Then the oxen pulled a large log across the field to make it level. Seed was scattered or "broadcast" by hand to the left and right as the farmer walked up and down the field. The oxen dragged a large branch over the sown ground to cover the seed. The farmer waited and hoped for good weather.

Pioneer Reading Activity Six: *(page 27)*
1. scythe   2. stooks   3. flail   4. sickle   5. flailer   6. cradle
7. threshing   8. gristmill   9. hominy block   10. winnowing   11. miller   12. bran
13. quern   14. millstones

Pioneer Reading Activity Seven: *(page 29)*
pigs: salt pork, lard, soap, candles, to sell
hens, ducks, turkeys: meat, eggs
horses, oxen: pull ploughs, sleighs, wagons, carriages, to ride
cat: to catch rats and mice
cattle: milk to drink, make butter, make cheese, meat
geese: meat, eggs, feathers, quill pens, pillows, mattresses, to sell

dogs: pull small sleds, protection, watchdog, chase strangers, foxes and other animals away
sheep: meat, wool

Pioneer Reading Activity Eight: *(page 31)*
1. False **2.** True **3.** False **4.** True **5.** False **6.** True **7.** False
8. True **9.** True **10.** True **11.** False **12.** True

Pioneer Reading Activity Nine: *(page 34)*
1. Past **2.** Present **3.** Present **4.** Past **5.** Present **6.** Past **7.** Present
8. Past **9.** Present **10.** Past **11.** Present **12.** Past

Pioneer Reading Activity Ten: *(page 36)*
A) 3, 5, 10, 6, 4, 2, 7, 1, 8, 9 **B)** 7, 4, 1, 3, 6, 5, 2, 8

Pioneer Reading Activity Eleven: *(page 39)*
1. they did not have many spices or sugar.
2. they had brought seeds with them.
3. sugar cane does not grow in North America. It had to be brought by ship.
4. the Native People had taught them how to tap the trees and to boil the sap.
5. the sap is running in the trees.
6. bits of bark and other dirt had to be removed.
7. it would burn.
8. they would lead them to a honey bee tree.
9. it made the bees sleepy and calm.
10. the pioneers would have plenty of honey and beeswax to make candles.

Pioneer Reading Activity Twelve: *(page 41)*
1. Candles and the fireplace
2. Tallow was used
3. Tallow candles did not
4. Candle wicks were tied
5. Lye and tallow were the two
6. The ashes from the fireplace
7. The rainwater dissolved the ashes
8. Lye-water, tallow, the fat scraps
9. The liquid became thick and hard
10. A pioneer family bathed

Pioneer Reading Activity Thirteen: *(page 44)*
1. hunting **2.** fishing **3.** trapping **4.** fishing **5.** trapping **6.** hunting **7.** fishing
8. hunting **9.** hunting or trapping **10.** fishing **11.** fishing **12.** hunting or trapping
13. hunting

Pioneer Reading Activity Fourteen: *(page 48)*
5, 8, 1, 7, 2, 9, 13, 10, 6, 4, 11, 3, 12

Pioneer Reading Activity Fifteen: *(page 51)*
1. They used the birchbark canoe and the dugout.
2. Canals were built so boats could go around rapids and could go from lake to lake.
3. Blazed trails are routes through the forests shown by notched trees made by the Native People.
4. They were bumpy, full of stumps and very muddy in the spring and summer.
5. A corduroy road is made of trees split in half. The trees are laid flat-side down close to each other.
6. Horses could slip, break a leg or trip and wagons lost wheels or they got stuck.
7. Plank roads were not as bumpy and much safer.
8. They had to build bridges.
9. They pulled carts, wagons, stagecoaches, carriages and sleighs from place to place.
10. The stagecoach carried travelers, supplies and the mail from town to town.

Pioneer Reading Activity Sixteen: *(page 53)*

1. Pioneer Boys
2. Pioneer Boys & Girls
3. Pioneer Girls
4. Pioneer Boys & Girls
5. Pioneer Girls
6. Pioneer Boys & Girls
7. Pioneer Boys
8. Pioneer Boys
9. Pioneer Girls
10. Pioneer Boys & Girls
11. Pioneer Girls
12. Pioneer Boys
13. Pioneer Boys & Girls
14. Pioneer Girls
15. Pioneer Girls
16. Pioneer Boys
17. Pioneer Girls
18. Pioneer Boys & Girls
19. Pioneer Girls
20. Pioneer Girls

Pioneer Reading Activity Seventeen: *(page 58)*

1. miller
2. General Store
3. sawmill
4. carpenter
5. blacksmith
6. gunsmith
7. farrier
8. silversmith, pewterer
9. tinsmith
10. cobbler
11. cooper
12. wheelwright
13. wainwright
14. storekeeper
15. dressmaker

Pioneer Reading Activity Eighteen: *(page 61)*

1. The children often had to
2. The pioneer community would work
3. The heat was not spread
4. The parents were to pay
5. Working at a backwoods school
6. Teachers were strict and ruled
7. The children sat on backless
8. The schools could not afford
9. The first reader that pioneer
10. They practiced the letters of
11. Students were often beaten for
12. When the pioneers first settled

Pioneer reading Activity Nineteen: *(page 64)*

A) 1. There was plenty of fresh air and bright sunshine.
2. There was no smog or polluted air.
3. The pioneers were in good physical shape because they walked everywhere and worked hard.
4. There were no chemicals or preservatives in their food.
5. They used trees, roots and herbs found in the forests to cure minor illnesses.

B) 1. Pioneers did not know that cleanliness prevented germs from spreading.
2. Their meals were not nutritious and lacked vitamins so their bodies couldn't fight off germs.
3. Their milk was full of germs because it was not pasteurized.
4. Some diseases were highly contagious and germs spread rapidly.
5. Rats and mice on sailing ships coming from Europe carried diseases.

C) *ague, *pneumonia, *mumps, *measles, * chicken pox, *tuberculosis

Pioneer Reading Activity Twenty: *(page 67)*

1. False <u>metal</u>
2. True
3. False <u>beaver meat</u>
4. False <u>poisonous</u>
5. False <u>beachnut</u>
6. True
7. True
8. False <u>pine</u>
9. False <u>moose</u>
10. False <u>snowshoes</u>
11. True
12. False <u>fish</u>
13. True
14. True

Pioneer Word Study Activity One: *(page 68)*

A) 2, 5, 3, 1, 4
B) 2, 5, 1, 4, 3
C) 5, 1, 3, 4, 2
D) 4, 1, 5, 2, 3
E) 5, 2, 4, 3, 1
F) 4, 5, 1, 3, 2
G) 3, 5, 1, 4, 2
H) 3, 5, 2, 4, 1
I) 4, 2, 3, 5, 1

Pioneer Word Study Activity Two: *(page 69)*

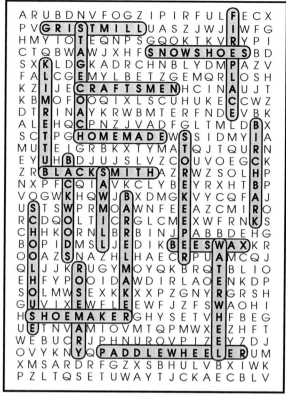

Pioneer Word Study Activity Three: *(page 70)*

Pioneer Word Study Activity Four: *(page 71)*
Underline One Syllable Words: lye, scythe, yoke, flail
Two Syllable Words: trencher, pestle, caldron, kettle
Three Syllable Words: petticoat, molasses, broadcasting, kerosene
Four Syllable Words: destination, epidemic, apprenticeship, persecuted

Pioneer Word Study Activity Five: *(page 72)*
1. flour   **2.** died, sea   **3.** pair   **4.** knead, dough   **5.** berries, ate   **6.** bare, their   **7.** Bean
8. moulds   **9.** Lye   **10.** deer, meat   **11.** wore, plain   **12.** beat   **13.** peeled   **14.** rode, sleigh

Pioneer Sounds Activity One: *(page 73)*
1. mm, ll   **2.** tt, bb, ll, zz, pp   **3.** mm, ff   **4.** dd, rr   **5.** dd, mm, mm, ll   **6.** ll, pp, nn, rr
7. ll, tt   **8.** ll, dd, bb, tt, ll   **9.** rr, gg   **10.** nn, tt, tt

Pioneer Sounds Activity Two: *(page 74)*
1. quack   **2.** quill   **3.** quiet   **4.** queer   **5.** quick   **6.** quern   **7.** queen
8. quail   **9.** quarter   **10.** quarrel   **11.** quit   **12.** quiz

Pioneer Sounds Activity Three: *(page 75)*
Long a - cradle, ladle, snare   Short a - paddle, candle, axes   Long e - knead, cheese, weaver
Short e - kettle, tent, shelter   Long i - light, Bible, winder   Short i - knitting, miller, tinsmith
Long o - hoe, bowls, pork   Short o - logging, cobbler, oxen   Long u - ague, use, community
Short u - stumps, sums, bush

Pioneer Sounds Activity Four: *(page 76)*
1. tr, st, sl   **2.** fl, gr, pl   **3.** bl, sm, sk, tr, cr, bl   **4.** gr, gr, fl   **5.** cl, tr, st, st, pl, cr   **6.** pl, bl, br
7. fr, st, sp   **8.** dr, sm, st   **9.** fl, cl, br   **10.** sp, tw   **11.** sl, st, sk, sp   **12.** sk, dr

Pioneer Sounds Activity Five: *(page 77)*
1. bushes   **2.** benches   **3.** berries   **4.** buggies   **5.** scarves   **6.** stagecoaches   **7.** geese
8. dresses   **9.** churches   **10.** stitches   **11.** groceries   **12.** ferries   **13.** harnesses   **14.** potatoes

Pioneer Language Activity One: *(page 78)*
1. when   **2.** where   **3.** what   **4.** how   **5.** how   **6.** when   **7.** what   **8.** who
9. why   **10.** where   **11.** where   **12.** why   **13.** where   **14.** who   **15.** where

                   SSF1-06

Pioneer Language Activity Two: (page 79)

1. (Pioneers) had to make (butter) in a wooden (churn.)
2. (Apples) were eaten fresh and baked in (pies) and other (desserts.)
3. They traded or bartered (butter) (eggs) and (vegetables) for (tools) (dishes) (cloth) (coffee) (sugar) and (spices.)
4. Once a (village) had a (sawmill) (logs) could be cut easily into (boards.)
5. (Kerosene) is a (kind) of (oil) that was burned in (lamps) for (light.)
6. Work (animals) such as (horses) and (oxen) pulled (wagons) and (ploughs.)
7. A (pedlar) travelled from (village) to (village) selling (goods) from his (wagon.)
8. A (quilt) is a (type) of (blanket) made from (scraps) of colorful (fabric.)
9. A one-room (cabin) was made from (logs) (mud) and tree (bark.)
10. (Women) tore old (cloths) into (rags) and braided them to make rag (rugs.)

Pioneer Language Activity Three: *(page 80)*

1. Exclamatory	**2.** Imperative	**3.** Statement	**4.** Interrogative
5. Exclamatory	**6.** Imperative	**7.** Interrogative	**8.** Statement

Pioneer Language Activity Four: *(page 81)*

1. "Look at what I bought from the pedlar!" cried Sarah excitedly.
2. What color will Martha dye her wool for her new quilt?
3. The storekeeper sold cotton fabric, buttons, thimbles, china dishes, apple peelers and school supplies.
4. "What do you have in your crock, Sarah?" asked the storekeeper.
5. How much does it cost to mail a letter in pioneer times?
6. The pioneer women collected flower heads, leaves, roots and tree bark to make dye.
7. "Watch out for the milk!" cried Meg, as she grabbed the bucket from under the cow.
8. The family packed warm clothes, heavy boots, pewter dishes, iron pots and frying pans into two, large, steamer trunks.
9. Billy followed the honey bee to a large, old, maple tree and found a hive full of honey.
10. "This maple syrup tastes delicious!" exclaimed Ben, as he hungrily ate the stack of steaming flapjacks.
11. The pioneers used horses to pull their wagons, stagecoaches, carriages and buggies.
12. "I think these tracks are the kind that lynx make," said Willie in a frightened voice.

Pioneer Language Activity Five: *(page 82)*

1. The (crackling) fire in the fireplace burned [merrily] during the (cold) (winter) evening.
2. The (pioneer) mother used her (left) foot to [gently] rock the (wooden) cradle while she peeled potatoes.
3. The (flickering) candle went out [suddenly] leaving the room in (total) darkness.
4. Mary's mother gently kneaded the (soft) dough so her bread would bake [lightly] and [airily.]
5. The (warm) (blackberry) pie that was sitting on the table smelled [heavenly.]
6. The (steaming) sap that was bubbling [steadily] over the fire had to be stirred [constantly] so it would not burn.
7. The (delicious) smell of (licorice) sticks and (saltwater) taffy made Joey's mouth water [terribly.]
8. The (huge) waterwheel was [slowly] turned by the (flowing) water from the (large) millpond.
9. The (beautiful) quilt that decorated Sarah's bed had been stitched [neatly] and [carefully.]
10. Hot water [slowly] dripped through the ashes producing a (thick) liquid called lye.

Pioneer Research Activities: *(page 83)*

Answers will vary.